A LEVEL
Questions and Answers

PURE MATHS

Peter Sherran & Janet Crawshaw

EDUCATIONAL

SERIES EDITOR: BOB McDUELL

Contents

Introduction

HOW TO USE THIS BOOK

The aim of the *Questions and Answers* series is to provide students with the help required to attain the highest level of achievement in important examinations. This book is intended to help you with the Pure Mathematics component of A- and AS-level Mathematics or, in Scotland, Higher Level Mathematics. The series relies on the idea that an experienced examiner can provide, through examination questions, sample answers and advice, the help students need to secure success. Many revision aids concentrate on providing factual information that might have to be recalled in an examination. This series, while giving factual information in an easy-to-remember form, concentrates on the other skills that need to be developed for the new A-level examinations which started in 1996.

The *Questions and Answers* series is designed to provide:

- Easy-to-use **Revision Summaries** that identify important factual information that students must understand if progress is to be made in answering examination questions.

- Advice on the different types of question in each subject and how to answer them well to obtain the highest marks.

- Information about other skills, apart from the recall of knowledge, that will be tested on examination papers. These are sometimes called **assessment objectives** and modern A-level examinations put great emphasis on them. The *Questions and Answers* series is intended to develop these skills, particularly of communication, problem-solving, evaluation and interpretation, by the use of questions and the appreciation of outcomes by the student.

- Many examples of **examination questions**. Students can increase their achievement by studying a sufficiently wide range of questions, provided that they are shown the way to improve their answers to these questions. It is advisable that students try the questions first before looking at the answers and the advice that accompanies them. All the Pure Mathematics questions come from actual examination papers or specimen materials issued by the British Examination Boards, reflecting their requirements.

- **Sample answers** and mark schemes to all the questions.

- **Advice from examiners**: by using the experience of actual examiners we are able to give advice that can enable students to see how their answers can be improved to ensure greater success.

Success in A-level examinations comes from proper preparation and a positive attitude, developed through a sound knowledge of facts and an understanding of principles. These books are intended to overcome 'examination nerves' which often come from a fear of not feeling properly prepared.

THE IMPORTANCE OF USING QUESTIONS FOR REVISION

Past examination questions play an important part in revising for examinations. However, it is important not to start practising questions too early. Nothing can be more disheartening than trying to do a question that you do not understand because you have not mastered the concepts. Therefore it is important to have studied a topic thoroughly before attempting questions on it.

It is unlikely that any question you try will appear in exactly the same form on the papers you are going to take. However the number of totally original questions that can be set on any part of the syllabus is limited and so similar ideas occur over and over again. It certainly will help you if the question you are trying to answer in an examination is familiar and you are used to the type of language used. Your confidence will be boosted, and confidence is important for examination success.

Practising examination questions will also highlight gaps in your knowledge and understanding that you can go back and revise more thoroughly. It will indicate which sorts of question you can do well and which, if there is a choice, you should avoid.

Finally, having access to answers, as you do in this book, will enable you to see clearly what is required by the examiner, how best to answer each question and the amount of detail required. Remember that attention to detail is a very important aspect of achieving success at A-level.

MAXIMISING YOUR MARKS IN PURE MATHEMATICS

One of the keys to examination success is to know how marks are gained or lost and the examiner's tips given with the solutions in this book give hints on how you can maximise your marks on particular questions. However you should also take careful note of these general points:

● Check the requirements of your examination board and follow the instructions (or 'rubric') carefully about the number of questions to be tackled. Many A-level Mathematics examinations instruct you to attempt all the questions and where papers start with short, straightforward questions, you are advised to work through them in order so that you build up your confidence. Do not overlook any parts of a question – double-check that you have seen everything, including any questions on the back page! If there is a choice, do the correct number. If you do more, you will not be given credit for any extra and it is likely that you will not have spent the correct time on each question and your answers could have suffered as a result. Take time to read through all the questions carefully, and then start with the question you think you can do best.

● Get into the habit of setting out your work neatly and logically. If you are untidy and disorganised you could penalise yourself by misreading your own figures or lose marks because your method is not obvious. Always show all necessary working so that you can obtain marks for a correct method even if your final answer is wrong. Remember that a good clear sketch can help you to see important details.

● When the question asks for a particular result to be established, remember that to obtain the method marks you must show sufficient working to convince the examiner that your argument is valid. Do not rely too heavily on your graphical calculator.

● Do not be sloppy with algebraic notation or manipulation, especially involving brackets and negatives. Do rough estimates of calculations to make sure that they are reasonable, state units if applicable and give answers to the required degree of accuracy; do not approximate prematurely in your working.

● Make sure that you are familiar with the formulas booklet and tables that you will be given in the examination and learn any useful formulas that are not included. Refer to the booklet in the examination and transfer details accurately.

● When about 15 minutes remain, check whether you are running short of time. If so, try to score as many marks as possible in the short time that remains, concentrating on the easier parts of any questions not yet tackled.

● The following glossary may help you in answering questions:
  Write down, state – no justification is needed for an answer.
  Calculate, find, determine, show, solve – include enough working to make your method clear.
  Deduce, hence – make use of the given statement to establish the required result.
  Sketch – show the general shape of a graph, its relationship with the axes, any asymptotes and points of special significance such as turning points.
  Draw – plot accurately, using graph paper and selecting a suitable scale; this is usually preparation for reading information from the graph.
  Find the <u>exact</u> value – leave it in fractions or surds, or in terms of logarithms, exponentials or π; note that using a calculator is likely to introduce decimal approximations, resulting in loss of marks.

Rules for indices

$$a^m \times a^n = a^{m+n} \qquad a^m \div a^n = a^{m-n} \qquad a^{mn} = (a^m)^n = (a^n)^m \qquad a^{\frac{1}{n}} = \sqrt[n]{a}$$

$$a^{\frac{m}{n}} = (a^m)^{\frac{1}{n}} = (a^{\frac{1}{n}})^m \qquad a^{-n} = \frac{1}{a^n} \qquad (ab)^n = a^n b^n \qquad \left(\frac{a}{b}\right)^n = \frac{a^n}{b^n}$$

Note, however, in general $(a+b)^n \neq a^n + b^n$ and $(a-b)^n \neq a^n - b^n$

Some important special cases are: $a^1 = a$ and, provided $a \neq 0$, $a^0 = 1$.

$$a^{-1} = \frac{1}{a} \text{ and } a^{\frac{1}{2}} = \sqrt{a} \quad (\text{Note: } a^{\frac{1}{2}} \times a^{\frac{1}{2}} = a^1 = a).$$

Logarithm is another word for **power**, **exponent** or **index**. The statement $10^2 = 100$ may be described by saying that the logarithm associated with 100, taking 10 as the **base**, is 2. This is usually written as $\log_{10} 100 = 2$. In general, $a^x = y \Leftrightarrow \log_a y = x$.

Natural logarithms have base $\mathbf{e} = 2.718\ 28...$ and are needed in order to integrate some types of **rational function**. The notation for natural logarithms is $\log_e x$ or $\ln x$.

The three basic laws of logarithms are: $\qquad \log_a x + \log_a y = \log_a xy$

$$\log_a x - \log_a y = \log_a \frac{x}{y}$$

$$\log_a x^n = n \log_a x$$

Logarithms may be used to solve **exponential equations** i.e. equations in which the unknown value is the exponent and to convert the graphs of exponential functions to **linear form**.

A function which is the sum of terms of the form ax^n, where n is a non-negative whole number and a is a constant, is called a **polynomial**. The highest value of n that occurs in the polynomial is known as the **degree** of the polynomial.

The remainder theorem states that when any polynomial function $f(x)$ is divided by $(x-r)$ the remainder is given by $f(r)$.

This approach enables us to find the remainder much quicker than by carrying out the division.

The factor theorem is simply a special case of this result corresponding to a remainder of zero. For any polynomial function $f(x)$, if $f(r) = 0$ then $(x-r)$ is a **factor** of $f(x)$.

The factor theorem may be applied to the solution of polynomial equations and to the sketching of associated graphs.

The **modulus** of a function $f(x)$ is denoted by $|f(x)|$ and takes the positive numerical value of $f(x)$.

This notation allows a condition such as $-1 < x < 1$ to be expressed simply as $|x| < 1$. The distance between two points, a and b, on the number line is given by the positive difference between a and b which may be written as $|a - b|$.

The graph of $y = |f(x)|$ is the same as the graph of $y = f(x)$ wherever $f(x) \geq 0$, but points where $f(x) < 0$ are reflected in the x-axis.

**REVISION
SUMMARY**

The general form of a **quadratic** function is $f(x) = ax^2 + bx + c$ (where $a \neq 0$). The graph of a quadratic function is always a **parabola**, which takes one of two possible forms depending on the sign of a (the coefficient of x^2).

Fig. 1 $a > 0$ $a < 0$

The roots of the quadratic equation $f(x) = 0$ are given by the intersection of the graph with the *x*-axis. These may be located approximately using a graphics calculator or computer graph plotter.

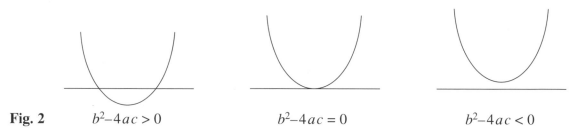

Fig. 2 $b^2 - 4ac > 0$ $b^2 - 4ac = 0$ $b^2 - 4ac < 0$

The diagrams above correspond to the situation where $a > 0$, but the principles apply equally when $a < 0$.

The solution of some quadratic equations may be found by **factorisation**.

$$2x^2 - 5x - 3 = 0 \Rightarrow (2x + 1)(x - 3) = 0 \Rightarrow 2x + 1 = 0 \text{ or } x - 3 = 0 \Rightarrow x = -\tfrac{1}{2} \text{ or } x = 3.$$

An alternative method that may be employed, even when factorisation is not possible, is known as **completing the square**. This involves re-writing an expression of the form $x^2 + bx + c$ as $(x + p)^2 + q$, which has the key advantage that the *unknown value only appears once*.

$$x^2 + 6x - 5 = 0 \Rightarrow (x + 3)^2 - 9 - 5 = 0 \qquad \text{Note: } (x + 3)^2 = x^2 + 6x + 9$$

$$\Rightarrow (x + 3)^2 - 14 = 0$$

$$\Rightarrow x + 3 = \pm\sqrt{14}$$

$$\Rightarrow x = -3 + \sqrt{14} \text{ or } x = -3 - \sqrt{14}$$

Note: $p = \tfrac{1}{2}b$ and $q = c - p^2$. However, if the process is applied to the general

quadratic $ax^2 + bx + c = 0$ then this leads to the formula $x = \dfrac{-b \pm \sqrt{b^2 - 4ac}}{2a}$.

In the formula, the value of $b^2 - 4ac$ is known as the **discriminant** and may be used to determine the nature of the roots as shown in Fig. 2.

$b^2 - 4ac > 0$ two distinct **real** roots.

$b^2 - 4ac = 0$ two **equal real** roots (i.e. the solution consists of a single value).

$b^2 - 4ac < 0$ two **complex** roots (i.e. the solution contains no real values).

REVISION SUMMARY

Another application of completing the square is in connection with **maximum** and **minimum** values of quadratic functions.

The *minimum* value of $(x + p)^2 + q$ occurs when $(x + p)^2 = 0$ i.e. when $x = -p$. It follows that q is the minimum value and that the lowest point on the graph of the function has coordinates $(-p, q)$.

Note: A function of the form $q - (x + p)^2$ has *maximum* value q when $x = -p$.

The most common *algebraic* approach to solving **simultaneous equations** initially involves reducing the set of equations to a single equation in one unknown. The two main methods of achieving this are:

❶ The **elimination** method – multiples of the equations are either added or subtracted in order to eliminate one of the unknown values.

$$2x + 3y = 7 \qquad (1)$$

$$3x - y = 5 \qquad (2)$$

Check that (1) + 3 × (2) gives $\qquad 11x = 22 \implies x = 2$.

Substituting for x in (2) now gives $\quad 6 - y = 5 \implies y = 1$.
(*Check* that these values work in (1)).

❷ The **substitution** method – one of the unknowns is made the subject of one of the equations and the result is substituted wherever the unknown appears.

From (2) $y = 3x - 5$. Substituting for y in (1) gives $2x + 3(3x - 5) = 7 \implies 11x - 15 = 7$.
From this point, the solution proceeds as before. The substitution method can also be used, for example, when only one equation is linear.

The manipulation of **inequalities** is much the same as the manipulation of equations apart from the complication that whenever a negative factor is introduced to both sides, the direction of the inequality is reversed. For example $-x > 2 \implies x < -2$. Care must also be taken when carrying out steps such as squaring both sides whenever negatives are involved.

If you need to revise this subject more thoroughly, see the relevant topics in the *Letts* A level *Mathematics Study Guide*.

Note: As an alternative to the strictly algebraic approach to the solution of equations and inequalities, graphs can be used to determine the nature, and approximate value, of the solutions. A graphics calculator is particularly useful, in this respect, and its trace and zoom facilities can often be used to locate these solutions to a high degree of accuracy. It is important, however, to include *details of the method* used in any solution.

Some functions of the form $\dfrac{p(x)}{q(x)}$ (where $p(x)$ and $q(x)$ are polynomials) are best expressed in **partial fractions** before we attempt to integrate them or work out their series expansions. The following forms, where the degree of $p(x) <$ degree $q(x)$, are particularly important:

$$\frac{p(x)}{(ax+b)(cx+d)} \equiv \frac{A}{ax+b} + \frac{B}{cx+d} \qquad\qquad \frac{p(x)}{(ax+b)(cx+d)^2} \equiv \frac{A}{ax+b} + \frac{B}{cx+d} + \frac{C}{(cx+d)^2}$$

$$\frac{p(x)}{(ax+b)(cx^2+d)} \equiv \frac{A}{ax+b} + \frac{Bx+C}{cx^2+d} \qquad\text{(You can *check* by drawing the graph of each side).}$$

Note: If degree $p(x) \geq$ degree $q(x)$ *then these results do not hold* and division must be carried out first.

1 Algebra

1 (i) Given that $a^k = \sqrt[3]{\left(a^4\right)} \div a$, find the value of k.

(ii) Given that $27^x = 9^{(x-1)}$, find the value of x. (8)

London Examinations

2 (a) Solve the equation $2x^{\frac{1}{3}} = x^{-\frac{2}{3}}$. (4)

(b) Use your calculator to find the value of y, correct to three significant figures, where $3^y = 6$. (5)

Oxford & Cambridge (MEI)

3 Two variable quantities x and y are related by the equation $y = a(b^x)$, where a and b are constants. When a graph is plotted showing values of $\ln y$ on the vertical axis and values of x on the horizontal axis, the points lie on a straight line having gradient 1.8 and crossing the vertical axis at the point $(0, 4.1)$. Find the values of a and b. (5)

UCLES

4 The population of a country has been recorded at 10 year intervals during this century. The figures, in millions given to the nearest million, for the years 1910 to 1960, are as follows.

Year	1910	1920	1930	1940	1950	1960
Population	37	44	53	64	77	93

One model for population size is given by $P_n = P_0 \times k^n$

where P_0 is the population at some starting date

P_n is the population n years later

and k is a constant.

(i) According to this model, what happens to the population in each of the cases

(A) $k > 1$ (B) $k = 1$ (C) $k < 1$? (3)

(ii) Complete the table below giving $\log_{10} P_n$ for different values of n. Notice that P_0 is taken to be the population in the year 1900 and so n is the number of years that have elapsed since 1900. (2)

Year	1910	1920	1930	1940	1950	1960
n	10	20				60
$\log_{10} P_n$	1.57					1.97

(iii) Draw the graph of $\log_{10} P_n$ against n on the axes given opposite. (2)

(iv) Explain how you can tell from the graph whether the given model gives a good description of the population. (2)

(v) Estimate the values of P_0 and k from your graph. (3)

The populations in 1970 to 1990 were as follows.

Year	1970	1980	1990
Population	110	125	138

(vi) Comment on the significance of these figures, bearing in mind the given model. (2)

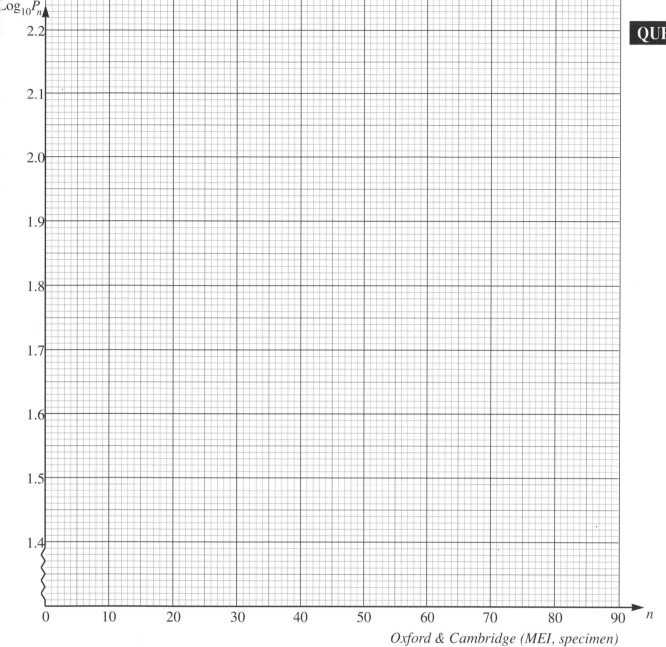

Oxford & Cambridge (MEI, specimen)

5 Given that $(x-2)$ and $(x+2)$ are each factors of x^3+ax^2+bx-4, find the values of a and b. (4)

For these values of a and b, find the other linear factor of x^3+ax^2+bx-4. (2)
UCLES

6 (a) Show that $(x+2)$ is a factor of the polynomial $f(x)$ given by

$$f(x)=2x^3-3x^2-11x+6.$$ (1)

(b) Express $f(x)$ as the product of three linear factors. (2)

(c) By considering the graph of $y=f(x)$, or otherwise, solve the inequality $f(x)\le 0$. (2)
NEAB

7 Express x^2-4x+9 in the form $(x-a)^2+b$, where a and b are constants. Hence, or

otherwise, state the maximum value of $f(x)=\dfrac{1}{x^2-4x+9}$. (3)
AEB

1 Algebra

8 Given that $(2x+1)$ is a factor of $2x^3 + ax^2 + 16x + 6$, show that $a = 9$. (2)

Find the real quadratic factor of $2x^3 + 9x^2 + 16x + 6$. By completing the square, or otherwise, show that this quadratic factor is positive for all real values of x. (4)

UCLES

9 (i) Sketch the graph of the function f where $f : x \longrightarrow |3x - 1|$ for all $x \in \mathbb{R}$ (3)

(ii) Find the *two* values of x such that $|3x - 1| = x$. (3)

(iii) Hence find the range of values of x for which $|3x - 1| > x$. (3)

NICCEA

10 (a) On the same diagram, sketch the graphs of

$$y = \frac{1}{x-a} \text{ and } y = 4|x-a|, \text{ where } a \text{ is a positive constant.}$$

Show clearly the coordinates of any points of intersection with the coordinate axes.

(b) Hence or otherwise, find the set of values of x for which $\dfrac{1}{x-a} < 4|x-a|$. (12)

London Examinations

11 Find the values of k for which the equation $2x^2 + 4x + k = 0$ has real roots. (2)

SEB

12 The quadratic equation $x^2 + 6x + 1 = k(x^2 + 1)$ has equal roots.
Find the possible values of the constant k. (4)

AEB

13 It is given that
$$f(x) = 4x^3 - 16x^2 - 19x - 5.$$

(a) Use the factor theorem to show that $(x - 5)$ and $(2x + 1)$ are factors of $f(x)$. (2)

(b) Factorise $f(x)$ completely. (2)

(c) (i) Using your answer to part (b), show that there is only one real value of t satisfying the equation
$$4e^{3t} - 16e^{2t} - 19e^t - 5 = 0$$ (2)

(ii) Calculate this value of t. (1)

NEAB

14 Solve the simultaneous equations
$$x + y = 2$$
$$x^2 + 2y^2 = 11.$$ (6)

UCLES

15 The straight line $y = x$ cuts the circle $x^2 + y^2 - 6x - 2y - 24 = 0$ at A and B.

(a) Find the coordinates of A and B. (3)

(b) Find the equation of the circle which has AB as diameter. (3)

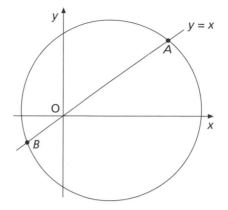

SEB

16 It is given that $y = 2 \log_a 12 - \log_a 9$

(a) Express y in the form $\log_a n$, where the value of n is to be determined. (2)

(b) Write down the value of y when $a = 2$. (1)

NEAB

17 (a) Express $\dfrac{1 - x - x^2}{(1 - 2x)(1 - x)^2}$ as the sum of three partial fractions. (4)

(b) Hence or otherwise, expand this expression in ascending powers of x up to and including the term in x^3. (5)

(c) State the range of values of x for which this expansion is valid. (1)

NEAB

18 (a) You are given that $f(x) = 2x^3 - x^2 - 7x + 6$.

(i) Show that $f(1) = 0$.

Hence find the three factors of $f(x)$. (4)

(ii) Solve the inequality $f(x) > 0$. (3)

(b) (i) Given that

$$\frac{x^2 + 2x + 7}{(2x + 3)(x^2 + 4)} \equiv \frac{A}{(2x + 3)} + \frac{Bx + C}{(x^2 + 4)}$$

find the values of the constants A, B and C. (3)

(ii) Use your answer to (b) (i) to find

$$\int \frac{x^2 + 2x + 7}{(2x + 3)(x^2 + 4)} \, dx.$$ (3)

Oxford & Cambridge (MEI)

19 $f(x) \equiv \dfrac{x^2 + 6x + 7}{(x + 2)(x + 3)}, \quad x \in \mathbb{R}$

Given that $f(x) \equiv A + \dfrac{B}{(x + 2)} + \dfrac{C}{(x + 3)}$,

(a) find the values of the constants A, B and C,

(b) show that $\displaystyle\int_0^2 f(x)\,dx = 2 + \ln\left(\frac{25}{18}\right)$. (11)

London Examinations

2 *Sequences and series*

A list of numbers in a particular order, and subject to some rule for obtaining subsequent values, is called a **sequence**. Each number in a sequence is called a **term**, and terms are often denoted by $u_1, u_2, u_3, ..., u_n, ...$

A sequence may be defined by

❶ Using a formula for the **general term**.

For example, substituting $n = 1, 2, 3, ...$ into the formula $u_n = n^2 + 1$ generates the sequence 2, 5, 10, 17, 26, ... In this way, the value of any term may be calculated directly by substituting its position into the formula. The 100th term, for example, would be given by $100^2 + 1 = 10\,001$.

❷ Using an **inductive definition**.

This describes how a given term relates to the previous term or terms e.g $u_{n+1} = 2u_n$. Such a description is known as a **recurrence relation** and requires knowledge of the value of some term, or terms, to be put into effect. In this example, given that $u_1 = 3$ would generate the sequence 3, 6, 12, 24, ... The **Fibonacci sequence** 1, 1, 2, 3, 5, 8, ..., on the other hand, may be defined by $u_{n+2} = u_{n+1} + u_n$ where $u_1 = 1, u_2 = 1$ i.e. knowledge of two consecutive terms is needed.

Sequences which carry on indefinitely are either convergent or divergent. In **convergent** sequences, terms approach a particular value known as a **limit**. The following sequences are convergent.

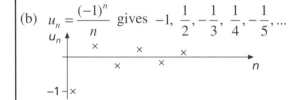

(a) $u_{n+1} = \dfrac{n+1}{n}$ gives $\dfrac{2}{1}, \dfrac{3}{2}, \dfrac{4}{3}, \dfrac{5}{4}, ...$

As $n \to \infty, u_n \to 1$. i.e. The limit is 1.

(b) $u_n = \dfrac{(-1)^n}{n}$ gives $-1, \dfrac{1}{2}, -\dfrac{1}{3}, \dfrac{1}{4}, -\dfrac{1}{5}, ...$

As $n \to \infty, u_n \to 0$. Note that this sequence oscillates about 0.

A sequence that does not converge to a limit is said to be **divergent**. The following sequences are divergent.

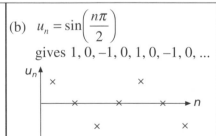

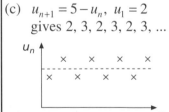

(a) $u_{n+1} = 2u_n, u_1 = 1$ gives 1, 2, 4, 8, 16, ...

This sequence may also be defined by $u_n = 2^{n-1}$.

(b) $u_n = \sin\left(\dfrac{n\pi}{2}\right)$ gives $1, 0, -1, 0, 1, 0, -1, 0, ...$

After every 4 terms, this sequence repeats itself. Its behaviour is described as **periodic** (with **period** 4).

(c) $u_{n+1} = 5 - u_n, u_1 = 2$ gives 2, 3, 2, 3, 2, 3, ...

Note that this sequence is both **oscillatory** (about 2.5) and periodic (with period 2).

Two special sequences are the **arithmetic progression** (A.P.) and the **geometric progression** (G.P.) In an A.P. successive terms have a **common difference** e.g. 1, 4, 7, 10, ...
In the usual notation, the first term and the common difference are denoted by a and d respectively. The inductive definition of an A.P. could be given as $u_{n+1} = u_n + d, \ u_1 = a$.

Thus, an A.P. takes the form $a, a + d, a + 2d, a + 3d, ...$ and the nth term is $u_n = a + (n-1)d$.

The inductive definition of a G.P. could be given as $u_{n+1} = ru_n$, $u_1 = a$. Thus a G.P. takes the form a, ar, ar^2, ar^3, ar^4,... where r is called the **common ratio** e.g. 1, 3, 9, 27, ... The nth term of a G.P. is given by $u_n = ar^{n-1}$.

A **series** is formed by adding together the terms of a sequence. The use of **sigma notation** can greatly simplify the way that series are written. For example, the series $1^2 + 2^2 + 3^2 + 4 + ... + n^2$ may be written as $\sum_{i=1}^{n} i^2$. The sum of the first n terms of a series is often denoted by S_n and so

$$S_n = u_1 + u_2 + u_3 + ... + u_n = \sum_{i=1}^{n} u_i.$$

The sum of an A.P. is given by $S_n = \dfrac{n}{2}(2a + (n-1)d)$ which may be written as $S_n = \dfrac{n}{2}(a + l)$ where l is the last term. In a given situation, one form may be more convenient to use than the other depending on the information available.

The sum of a G.P. is given by $S_n = \dfrac{a(1 - r^n)}{1 - r}$ or alternatively by $S_n = \dfrac{a(r^n - 1)}{r - 1}$. The choice of which formula to use depends on the value of r and only amounts to avoiding minus signs. Provided that $|r| < 1$, the sum of a G.P. converges to $\dfrac{a}{1 - r}$ as $n \to \infty$. This is sometimes written as $S_\infty = \dfrac{a}{1 - r}$.

When n is a positive integer, the **binomial expansion** of $(1 + x)^n$ is given by

$$(1 + x)^n = 1 + nx + \frac{n(n-1)x^2}{2!} + \frac{n(n-1)(n-2)x^3}{3!} + ...$$

In this case, the expansion contains $n + 1$ terms (the last of which is x^n) and is valid for *all* x.

Each term is of the form $\binom{n}{r} x^r$ where $\binom{n}{r} = \dfrac{n(n-1)...(n-r+1)}{r!}$ and so $(1 + x)^n = \sum_{r=0}^{n} \binom{n}{r} x^r$.

The first term corresponds to $r = 0$, the second term to $r = 1$ and so on. (Note that $0! = 1$). This form tends to be used more for finding particular terms than for working out the full expansion.

If n is *not* a positive integer then the expansion continues indefinitely and is *only valid for* $|x| < 1$.

e.g. Expanding $(1 - x)^{-1}$ we obtain the series $1 + x + x^2 + x^3 + x^4 + ...$

The significance of the condition that $|x| < 1$ might be seen by substituting particular values of x.

When $x = \frac{1}{2}$ this produces $2 = 1 + \frac{1}{2} + \frac{1}{4} + \frac{1}{8} + ...$ (Note: this is the result we would expect for the sum of an infinite G.P. with $a = 1$ and $r = \frac{1}{2}$).

However, taking $x = 2$, $(1 - x)^{-1} = -1$ and this is *not* the same as

$1 + x + x^2 + x^3 + ... = 1 + 2 + 2^2 + 2^3 + ...$ which is seen to be divergent.

For *small values of x*, the first few terms of an infinite series may provide a good **approximation to a function**. For example, using the binomial expansion, $\sqrt{1 + x} \approx 1 + \dfrac{x}{2} - \dfrac{x^2}{8}$.

Some important examples, based on the **Maclaurin expansion**, are:

$\sin x \approx x$, $\cos x \approx 1 - \dfrac{x^2}{2}$, $\tan x \approx x$. Note that, in each case, x is in **radians**.

2 Sequences and series

1 (i) The tenth term of an arithmetic progression is 36, and the sum of the first ten terms is 180. Find the first term and the common difference. (4)

(ii) Evaluate $\displaystyle\sum_{r=1}^{1000}(3r-1)$. (3)

UCLES

2 (a) A geometric progression has non-zero first term a and common ratio r, where $0 < r < 1$. Given that the sum of the first 8 terms of the progression is equal to half the sum to infinity, find the value of r, correct to 3 decimal places. (3)

Given also that the 17th term of the progression is 10, find a. (2)

(b) An arithmetic progression has first term a and common difference 10. The sum of the first n terms of the progression is 10 000. Express a in terms of n, and show that the nth term of the progression is

$$\frac{10\ 000}{n}+5(n-1).$$

(3)

Given that the nth term is less than 500, show that $n^2-101n+2000 < 0$, and hence find the largest possible value of n. (4)

UCLES

3 A small ball is dropped from a height of 1 m on to a horizontal floor. Each time the ball strikes the floor it rebounds to $\frac{3}{5}$ of the height it has fallen.

(a) Show that, when the ball strikes the floor for the third time, it has travelled a distance of 2.92 m.

(b) Show that the total distance travelled by the ball cannot exceed 4 m. (7)

London Examinations

4 Given that $(1+kx)^8 = 1+12x+px^2+qx^3+...$, for all $x \in \mathbb{R}$

(a) find the value of k, the value of p and the value of q.

(b) Using your values of k, p and q find the numerical coefficient of the x^3 term in the expansion of $(1-x)(1+kx)^8$. (11)

London Examinations

5 Write down the expansion of $(1+x)^5$. (1)

Hence, by letting $x = z+z^2$, find the coefficient of z^3 in the expansion of $(1+z+z^2)^5$ in powers of z. (4)

UCLES

6 (i) Expand $(1-2x)^{\frac{1}{2}}$ in ascending powers of x up to and including the term in x^4 and state the range for which this expansion is valid. (6)

(ii) Use this expansion to deduce the square root of 0.8 correct to *four* decimal places. (4)

NICCEA

7 Given that $|x| < \frac{1}{4}$, write down the expansion of $(1-4x)^{-\frac{1}{2}}$ in ascending powers

of x up to and including the term in x^3. (4)

Hence obtain the coefficient of x^3 in the expansion of $\dfrac{(1-3x)}{\sqrt{(1-4x)}}$. (2)

AEB

8 The nth terms of two sequences are defined as follows:

(a) $t_n = 1 - \dfrac{1}{n}$ (1)

(b) $u_n = 1 - \dfrac{1}{u_{n-1}}$, where $u_1 = 2$. (3)

Decide in each case whether the sequence is convergent, divergent or oscillating or periodic, giving reasons for your answers.

Oxford

9 (a) A geometric progression has first term a and common ratio r, where $0 < r < 1$ and a is non-zero.

   (i) The second term squared is equal to the fourth term and the sum to infinity is 1.

   Find a and r. (8)

   (ii) Show that the sum of the first 10 terms of this geometric progression is greater than 0.999. (4)

(b) (i) Find expressions for the nth term and the sum to n terms of the following arithmetic progression,

$$\log_e y + \log_e y^2 + \log_e y^3 + \ldots, \text{ where } y > 0.$$ (6)

   (ii) Hence find expressions for the nth term and the sum to n terms of the following arithmetic progression,

$$\log_e (xy) + \log_e (xy^2) + \log_e (xy^3) + \ldots, \text{ where } x > 0 \text{ and } y > 0.$$ (7)

NICCEA

10 The owner of a car has the car valued for insurance purposes on the same date every year.

The car was valued at £5000 in 1990. Each year since then the value of the car has been estimated at $£u_n$, where n is the number of years that have elapsed since 1990. The successive valuations are modelled by a law of the form

$$u_{n+1} = au_n + b,$$

where a and b are constants.

(a) Find the value of the car in 1993 according to each of the following models:

   Model 1: $a = 1$ and $b = -500$,

   Model 2: $a = 0.9$ and $b = 0$,

   Model 3: $a = 0.8$ and $b = 400$. (4)

(b) The owner of the car calculates that by 1998 it will be worth approximately £2150. Determine which of the above models he is using. (2)

(c) If Model 3 is used, the value of the car will converge to a limit, £V.

   (i) Write down an equation for V. (1)

   (ii) Calculate the limiting value of the car using this model. (1)

NEAB

11 For positive integers r, let

$$f(r) = \frac{1}{r(r+1)}$$

(a) Verify that $f(r) - f(r+1) = \dfrac{2}{r(r+1)(r+2)}$ (2)

(b) Hence find the sum of the first n terms of the series

$$\frac{1}{1.2.3} + \frac{1}{2.3.4} + \ldots + \frac{1}{r(r+1)(r+2)} + \ldots$$ (3)

Oxford

13

3 *Coordinate geometry*

To find the **distance between two points**, use Pythagoras' Theorem where

$$d = \sqrt{(x_2 - x_1)^2 + (y_2 - y_1)^2}$$

The **gradient** at a point on a line or a curve is the **rate of change of y in relation to x** at that point.

The **gradient of a line** is constant and it is often denoted by m where $m = \dfrac{y_2 - y_1}{x_2 - x_1}$.

The **mid-point** of the line joining (x_1, y_1) and (x_2, y_2) is $(\frac{1}{2}(x_1 + x_2); \frac{1}{2}(y_1 + y_2))$.

The most general format of the **equation of a line** is $ax + by + c = 0$. However the form that is often more useful is $y = mx + c$ where m is the gradient and c is the value of y when $x = 0$, i.e. the y-intercept. In this format it is easy to sketch lines provided that you remember the direction of the slope.

To find the equation of a line given the gradient m and a point (x_1, y_1) on the line,

- use $y = mx + c$, substituting the values for x_1 and y_1 to obtain c, or
- use $y - y_1 = m(x - x_1)$.

To find the equation of a line given two points (x_1, y_1) and (x_2, y_2) on the line, work out the gradient and then proceed as above.

Given two lines with gradients m_1 and m_2

- the lines are **parallel** if $m_1 = m_2$ (i.e. the gradients are the same),
- the lines are **perpendicular** if $m_1 \times m_2 = -1$ (i.e. the product of the gradients is -1).

See also:
Functions,
Unit 4.

Make sure that you are familiar with the general shape of the following **common curves**:

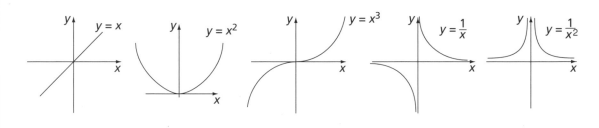

If you need to revise this subject more thoroughly, see the relevant topics in the

A level EDUCATIONAL *Mathematics Study Guide.*

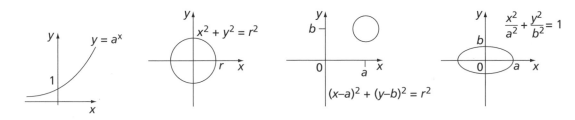

Parametric equations can be used to draw graphs. The x- and y-coordinates are each written in terms of a third variable, called a **parameter.**

For example, to draw $x = 4 + t$, $y = t^2$, find the coordinates by substituting various values of t. This process can be performed on a graphics calculator.

1 The points P, Q and R have coordinates $(2, 4)$, $(7, -2)$ and $(6, 2)$ respectively.

Find the equation of the straight line l which is perpendicular to the line PQ and which passes through the mid-point of PR. (5)

AEB

2 Find the equation of the straight line that passes through the points $(3, -1)$ and $(-2, 2)$, giving your answer in the form $ax + by + c = 0$. (3)

Hence find the coordinates of the points of intersection of the line and the x-axis. (2)

UCLES

3 The point A has coordinates $(2, -5)$. The straight line $3x + 4y - 36 = 0$ cuts the x-axis at B and the y-axis at C. Find

(a) the equation of the line through A which is perpendicular to the line BC; (2)

(b) the perpendicular distance from A to the line BC; (3)

(c) the area of triangle ABC. (2)

Oxford

4 The line l has equation $2x - y - 1 = 0$. The line m passes through the point $A(0, 4)$ and is perpendicular to the line l.

(a) Find an equation of m and show that the lines l and m intersect at the point $P(2, 3)$.

The line n passes through the point $B(3, 0)$ and is parallel to m.

(b) Find an equation of n and hence find the coordinates of the point Q where the lines l and n intersect.

(c) Prove that $AP = BQ = PQ$. (12)

London Examinations

5 A, B and C are the points $(0, 2)$ $(5, 7)$ and $(12, 0)$ respectively.

(i) Find the lengths AB, BC and CA of the sides of the triangle ABC, and show that $AB^2 + BC^2 = CA^2$. (4)

Deduce the size of angle ABC. (1)

(ii) Find the gradients of the lines AB and BC and show how these can be used to confirm your answer in part (i) for the size of angle ABC. (3)

(iii) M is the mid-point of line CA. Show that $MA = MB$. (3)

(iv) Hence write down, but do not simplify, the equation of the circle through A, B and C. (3)

Oxford & Cambridge (MEI, specimen)

6 (a) Find an equation of the line l which passes through the points $A(1, 0)$ and $B(5, 6)$.

The line m with equation $2x + 3y = 15$ meets l at point C.

(b) Determine the coordinates of C.

The point P lies on m and has x-coordinate -3.

(c) Show, by calculation, that $PA = PB$. (10)

London Examinations

4 Functions

**REVISION
SUMMARY**

A **function** may be thought of as a rule which assigns a *unique* value to each element of a given set.

$$x \longrightarrow \boxed{\text{function}} \longrightarrow y$$

The assigned value, in this case *y*, is referred to as the **image** of *x* under the function and may be denoted by $f(x)$, read as '*f* of *x*'. The set of values on which the function acts is called the **domain** and the corresponding set of image values is called the **range**. If for each element *y* in the range, there is a *unique* value of *x* such that $f(x)=y$ then *f* is a **one-one** function. If for any element *y* in the range, there is more than one value of *x* satisfying $f(x)=y$ then *f* is **many-one**.

The function which adds 7 to the square of every real number, for example, might be written as

$$f(x) = x^2 + 7, \ x \in \mathbb{R} \quad \text{or alternatively as} \quad f : x \to x^2 + 7, \ x \in \mathbb{R} \qquad \text{(} f \text{ is many-one)}.$$

The range of *f*, in this case, is given by $\{x : x \geq 7\}$.   (Note: This is the same as $\{y : y \geq 7\}$).

In some cases, particular values must be omitted from the domain for the function to be valid.

For example, $f(x) = \dfrac{x+2}{x-3}, \ x \in \mathbb{R} \ x \neq 3$ (division by zero is undefined).

If *f* and *g* are two functions then the **composite** function *fg* (sometimes written as $f \circ g$) is found by applying *g* first, followed by *f*, i.e. $fg(x) = f(g(x))$. It follows that the range of *g* becomes the domain of *f*.

$$x \xrightarrow{\quad g \quad} g(x) \xrightarrow{\quad f \quad} fg(x)$$

The *order* in which the functions are applied is very important. For example, if $f(x) = x^2$ and $g(x) = x - 1$, then $fg(x) = f(x-1) = (x-1)^2$ whereas $gf(x) = g(x^2) = x^2 - 1$.

If *g* is a function such that $gf(x) = x$ for all values *x* in the domain of *f*, then the effect of *g* is to *undo* what *f* has done and *g* is described as the **inverse** of *f*, denoted by f^{-1}. Only one-one functions have an inverse function, otherwise when the process is reversed the image may not be *unique*. One way to avoid this problem is to restrict the domain of the original function. For example, if $f(x) = \sin x$, where *x* can take all real values, then *f* does not have an inverse function. However, if the domain of *f* is restricted to $\{x : -90° \leq x \leq 90°\}$ then the inverse function exists.

The notation $\sin^{-1}(x)$ or arc sin *x* is used to denote this important function.

**If you need to
revise this
subject more
thoroughly,
see the relevant
topics in the
Letts A level
Mathematics
Study Guide.**

The graphs of some functions can be obtained by **transforming** the graph of a given function.

Function	Transformation of the graph of $y = f(x)$
$y = f^{-1}(x)$	Reflection in the line $y = x$.
$y = f(x) + a$	Translation described by $\begin{pmatrix} 0 \\ a \end{pmatrix}$
$y = af(x)$	One way stretch with scale factor *a* from $y = 0$.
$y = f(x - a)$	Translation described by $\begin{pmatrix} a \\ 0 \end{pmatrix}$
$y = f(ax)$	One-way stretch with scale factor $\frac{1}{a}$ from $x = 0$.

See also:
Coordinate
geometry,
Unit 3.

1 The function f is defined by

$$f : x \mapsto \frac{1}{2-x} + 3, \quad x \in \mathbb{R}, \quad x \neq 2$$

(a) Calculate $f(5)$ and $ff(5)$.

State the value of k $(k \neq 2)$ for which $ff(k)$ is not defined. (2)

(b) The inverse of f is f^{-1}. Find an expression for $f^{-1}(x)$ and state the domain of f^{-1}. (3)

AEB

2 $f(x) = 2x - 1$, $g(x) = 3 - 2x$ and $h(x) = \frac{1}{4}(5 - x)$.

(a) Find a formula for $k(x)$ where $k(x) = f(g(x))$. (2)

(b) Find a formula for $h(k(x))$. (2)

(c) What is the connection between the functions h and k? (1)

SEB

3 The functions f and g are defined by

$$f : x \mapsto 3x - 1, \quad x \in \mathbb{R}$$

$$g : x \mapsto x^2 + 1, \quad x \in \mathbb{R}$$

(a) Find the range of g.

(b) Determine the values of x for which $gf(x) = fg(x)$.

(c) Determine the values of x for which $|f(x)| = 8$.

The function $h : x \mapsto x^2 + 3x, \ x \in \mathbb{R}, \ x \geq q$, is one-one.

(d) Find the least value of q and sketch the graph of this function. (13)

London Examinations

4 The function f has domain the set of all non-zero real numbers, and is given by $f(x) = \dfrac{1}{x}$ for all x in this set. On a single diagram, sketch each of the following graphs, and indicate the geometrical relationships between them.

(i) $y = f(x)$,

(ii) $y = f(x+1)$,

(iii) $y = f(x+1) + 2$. (5)

Deduce, explaining your reasoning, the coordinates of the point about which the graph of $y = \dfrac{2x+3}{x+1}$ is symmetrical. (3)

UCLES

5 The function f with domain $\{x : x \geq 0\}$ is defined by $f(x) = 4x^2 - 1$.

(a) State the range of f and sketch the graph of f. (1)

(b) Explain why the inverse function f^{-1} exists and find $f^{-1}(x)$. (3)

(c) Given that g has domain $\{x : x \geq 0\}$ and is defined by $g(x) = \sqrt{(x+6)}$, solve the inequality

$$fg(x) \geq f(x).$$ (3)

Oxford

5 Trigonometry

Angles are measured in **degrees** or **radians**. One complete revolution of 360° is equivalent to 2π radians and one radian is about 57°. Make sure that your calculator is set to the required mode, remembering in particular that for all calculus operations, you must be in radians. You should learn the most common conversions:

$\frac{\pi}{6} = 30°, \frac{\pi}{4} = 45°, \frac{\pi}{3} = 60°, \frac{\pi}{2} = 90°, \frac{2\pi}{3} = 120°, \frac{3\pi}{4} = 135°, \frac{5\pi}{6} = 150°, \pi = 180°, \frac{3\pi}{2} = 270°$

When θ is measured in radians,
arc length, $s = r\theta$

area of sector $= \frac{1}{2}r^2\theta$.

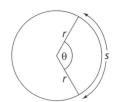

You should be able to solve trigonometry problems in 2 or 3 dimensions, recalling the sin, cos and tan ratios in right-angled triangles and the following rules that apply in *any* triangle.

Sine Rule: $\dfrac{a}{\sin A} = \dfrac{b}{\sin B} = \dfrac{c}{\sin C}$

Cosine Rule: $a^2 = b^2 + c^2 - 2bc \cos A$

Area of $\triangle ABC = \frac{1}{2}ab \sin C$

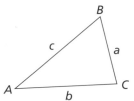

Be aware of the **ambiguous case of the sine rule**. This arises because there are two solutions between 0° and 180° of the equation $\sin \theta = c$, for example $\sin \theta = 0.5 \Rightarrow \theta = 30°$ or 150°. Sometimes one of the solutions can be eliminated (since the smallest angle is opposite the smallest side and the largest opposite the largest side), but there are occasions when both answers are possible.

It is useful to remember the following **special trigonometric ratios**, especially when you are required to give *exact* answers. You should also know the corresponding results for radians.

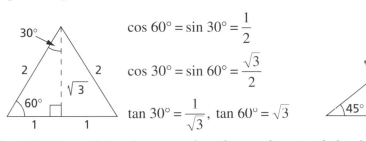

$\cos 60° = \sin 30° = \dfrac{1}{2}$

$\cos 30° = \sin 60° = \dfrac{\sqrt{3}}{2}$

$\tan 30° = \dfrac{1}{\sqrt{3}}, \tan 60° = \sqrt{3}$

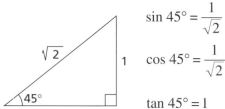

$\sin 45° = \dfrac{1}{\sqrt{2}}$

$\cos 45° = \dfrac{1}{\sqrt{2}}$

$\tan 45° = 1$

The definitions of the trigonometric ratios can be extended to include **any angle**, positive or negative, and you must make sure that you are familiar with the **graphs of sin θ, cos θ** and **tan θ**. They are all **periodic**, with $\sin \theta$ and $\cos \theta$ having period 360° (2π) and $\tan \theta$ having period 180° (π); $\sin \theta$ and $\cos \theta$ take values between −1 and 1; the range of $\tan \theta$ is unlimited.

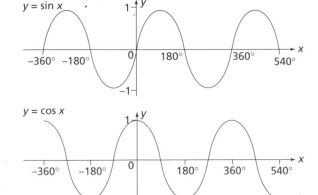

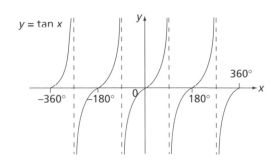

**REVISION
SUMMARY**

Remember that

$$\tan \theta = \frac{\sin \theta}{\cos \theta}, \qquad \operatorname{cosec} \theta = \frac{1}{\sin \theta}, \qquad \sec \theta = \frac{1}{\cos \theta}, \qquad \cot \theta = \frac{\cos \theta}{\sin \theta}.$$

We can see from the **periodic** and **symmetric properties** of the trigonometric functions that there are many solutions to equations such as $\sin \theta = 0.5$. Your calculator will give just one, in this case $\sin^{-1} 0.5 = 30°$ ($\pi/6$) known as the **principal value** of θ. For the sin and tan functions, the principal value lies between $-90°$ and $90°$ ($-\pi/2$ and $\pi/2$) and for the cos function, between $0°$ and $180°$ (0 and π). You will need to be proficient at working out other angles, usually in a specified range, once the principal value is known. All possible solutions can be summarised in the form of a **general solution**.

● To solve $\cos 2\theta = 0.5$ in the range $0 < \theta < 2\pi$, first find values of 2θ in the range $0 < 2\theta < 4\pi$. These are $2\theta = \pi/3, 2\pi - \pi/3, 2\pi + \pi/3, 4\pi - \pi/3,$
  i.e $2\theta = \pi/3, 5\pi/3, 7\pi/3, 11\pi/3 \Rightarrow \theta = \pi/6, 5\pi/6, 7\pi/6, 11\pi/6.$

Learn the basic **Pythagorean identity** $\sin^2 \theta + \cos^2 \theta \equiv 1$, from which the following can be deduced: $\tan^2 \theta + 1 \equiv \sec^2 \theta$ and $1 + \cot^2 \theta \equiv \operatorname{cosec}^2 \theta$. These are often needed when proving identities or solving equations.

● To solve $6\cos^2 \theta + \sin \theta = 5$, substitute $1 - \sin^2 \theta$ for $\cos^2 \theta$ and solve the quadratic equation in $\sin\theta$ so formed.

In the **addition formula** a common mistake is to write $\sin (A + B)$ as $\sin A + \sin B$, so you must be very clear that $\sin (A + B) \equiv \sin A \cos B + \cos A \sin B$. Make sure that you are familiar with the expansions of $\sin (A \pm B)$, $\cos (A \pm B)$ and $\tan (A \pm B)$. In particular, note that $\tan (A - B)$ is useful when finding the angle between two lines.

An important application of the addition formulae is that it allows functions of the type $a \cos \theta \pm b \sin \theta$ to be written in the form $R \cos (\theta \mp \alpha)$ and $a \sin \theta \pm b \cos \theta$ to be written in the form $R \sin (\theta \pm \alpha)$, with $R - \sqrt{a^2 + b^2}$ and $\tan \alpha - b/a$. Note that thc maximum and minimum values are given by $\pm R$.

● The maximum value of $f(\theta) = 3 \cos \theta + 4 \sin \theta$ is $\sqrt{3^2 + 4^2} = 5$ and the minimum value is -5.

● To sketch the curve, write it as $f(\theta) = 5 \cos (\theta - \alpha)$ where $\tan \alpha = \frac{4}{3} \Rightarrow \alpha = 53.1°$. Note that the curve is a transformation of $y = \cos \theta$, applying a one-way stretch with scale factor 5 from $y = 0$ (changing the amplitude to 5) and translating it by $53.1°$ to the right.

● To solve $3 \cos \theta + 4 \sin \theta = 2$, write it as $5 \cos (\theta - \alpha) = 2 \Rightarrow \cos (\theta - \alpha) = 0.4$, with $\alpha = 53.1°$. The advantage of this format is that θ appears only once in the equation.

Substituting $B = A$ in the addition formulae gives the **double angle** rules which are very important. Remember that $\sin 2A \equiv 2 \sin A \cos A$, $\tan 2A \equiv \dfrac{2 \tan A}{1 - \tan^2 A}$ and that $\cos 2A$ can be written in three different formats, where $\cos 2A \equiv 2\cos^2 A - 1 \equiv 1 - 2\sin^2 A \equiv \cos^2 A - \sin^2 A$. It is very useful to remember that $\cos^2 A \equiv \frac{1}{2} (1 + \cos 2A)$ and $\sin^2 A \equiv \frac{1}{2} (1 - \sin 2A)$.

● To solve $\sin 2x = \sqrt{3} \sin x$, write it as $2\sin x \cos x - \sqrt{3} \sin x = 0 \Rightarrow \sin x(2\cos x - \sqrt{3}) = 0,$

  so either $\sin x = 0$ or $\cos x = \sqrt{3}/2$. Do not be tempted to 'cancel' the factor of $\sin x$ which would result in the loss of the solutions relating to $\sin x = 0$.

For **small angles** θ, measured in radians, $\sin \theta \approx \theta$, $\tan \theta \approx \theta$, and $\cos \theta \approx 1 - \frac{1}{2}\theta^2$.

If you need to
revise this
subject more
thoroughly,
see the relevant
topics in the
Letts A level
*Mathematics
Study Guide.*

5 Trigonometry

1 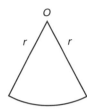 The diagram shows a sector of a circle, with centre O and radius r. The length of the arc is equal to half the perimeter of the sector. Find the area of the sector in terms of r. (3)

UCLES

2 The diagram shows a triangle ABC in which $AB = 5$ cm, $AC = BC = 3$ cm. The circle, centre A, radius 3 cm, cuts AB at X; the circle, centre B, radius 3 cm, cuts AB at Y.

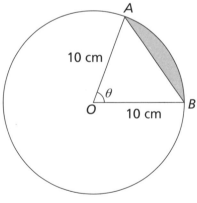

(a) Determine the size of the angle CAB, giving your answer in radians to four decimal places. (1)

(b) The region R, shaded in the diagram, is bounded by the arcs CX, CY and the straight line XY.

Calculate

(i) the length of the perimeter of R; (1)

(ii) the area of the sector ACX; (1)

(iii) the area of the region R. (2)

Oxford

3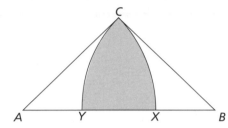

The diagram shows a circle centre O, radius 10 cm. AB is a chord and angle AOB is θ radians. Use the formula for the area of a sector to show that the area of the minor segment cut off by the chord AB (and shown shaded in the diagram) is $50(\theta - \sin \theta)$ cm². (3)

You are given that the shaded area is one-twentieth of the total area of the circle.

(i) Show that $\sin \theta = \theta - \frac{1}{10}\pi$. (2)

(ii) Check that $\theta = 1.27$ satisfies the equation approximately. (2)

(iii) Deduce the approximate value of angle AOB in degrees. (2)

Oxford & Cambridge

4 (a) Find the values of $\cos x$ for which
$$6 \sin^2 x = 5 + \cos x.$$

(b) Find all the values of x in the interval $180° < x < 540°$ for which
$$6 \sin^2 x = 5 + \cos x.$$
(8)

London Examinations

5 In triangle ABC, $AB = 8$ cm, $BC = 6$ cm and angle $B = 30°$.

    (a) Find the length of AC.   (3)

    (b) Find the size of angle A.   (3)

    Oxford

6 Let

$$f(A) = \frac{\cos A}{1 + \sin A} + \frac{1 + \sin A}{\cos A}$$

    (a) Prove that $f(A) = 2 \sec A$.   (3)

    (b) Solve the equation $f(A) = 4$,
        giving your answers for A, in degrees, in the interval $0° < A < 360°$.   (2)

    Oxford

7 Prove that $\sin 3\theta = 3 \sin \theta - 4 \sin^3 \theta$.   (3)

  Hence find all values of θ, for $0° \le \theta \le 360°$, which satisfy the equation $\sin 3\theta = 2 \sin \theta$.   (5)

    UCLES

8 (a) For the function $f(x) = \cos x° - \tan x°$, write down the values of x in the interval from -180 to 360 for which the function is undefined.   (1)

    (b) On the same axes, sketch the graphs of $y = \cos x°$ and $y = \tan x°$ for $-180 \le x \le 360$.   (1)

    (c) Use your sketch to determine the number of roots of the equations $f(x) = 0$ in the interval $-180 \le x \le 360$.   (1)

    (d) Find pairs of successive integers between which the roots lie.   (2)

    Oxford

9 Solve the equation $4 \tan^2 x + 12 \sec x + 1 = 0$, giving all solutions in degrees, to the nearest degree, in the interval $-180° < x < 180°$.   (6)

    AEB

10 The diagram shows the graph of the function $y = a + b\sin cx$ for $0 \le x \le \pi$.

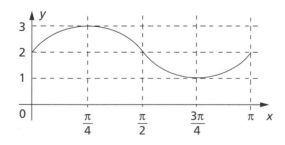

    (a) Write down the values of a, b and c.   (3)

    (b) Find algebraically the values of x for which $y = 2·5$.   (3)

    SEB

6 Differentiation

The **gradient of the curve** $y = f(x)$ at the point $P(x, y)$ is given by the gradient of the **tangent** at P.

To find this *geometrically*, consider the gradients of a sequence of chords PQ such that as $Q \to P$, the chord $PQ \to$ the tangent at P.

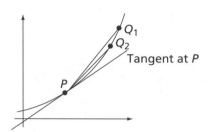

The gradient can be found *algebraically* from the **gradient function** of $y = f(x)$, written $\dfrac{dy}{dx}$, $\dfrac{d}{dx}(f(x))$ or $f'(x)$

To obtain the gradient function from **first principles** use:

$$f'(x) = \lim_{h \to 0} \frac{f(x+h) - f(x)}{h}$$

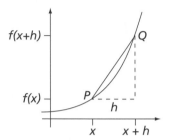

The process of finding the gradient function is called **differentiation**, where $\dfrac{dy}{dx}$ is the **derivative**, or **differential**, of y with respect to x. It gives the **rate of change** of y with respect to x. If $\dfrac{dy}{dx} > 0$, the function is increasing and if $\dfrac{dy}{dx} < 0$, the function is decreasing.

When differentiating from first principles, we use the limit definition. More often, though, we quote and use standard results and it is likely that in an examination you will be given many of these in a reference booklet. Make sure that you are familiar with them, using the booklet only for a final check on accuracy, not for inspiration!

You will know that if $y = kx^n$, then $\dfrac{dy}{dx} = nkx^{n-1}$. This rule is easy to apply, but care must be taken with negative and fractional indices:

$$y = \frac{1}{\sqrt{x}} + \frac{4}{x^2} = x^{-1/2} + 4x^{-2}, \quad \frac{dy}{dx} = -\frac{1}{2}x^{-3/2} - 8x^{-3} = -\frac{1}{2x^{3/2}} - \frac{8}{x^3}$$

Some expressions can be simplified first before differentiating, such as

$$\frac{d}{dx}\left(\frac{(3x-1)(x+2)}{x}\right) = \frac{d}{dx}\left(\frac{3x^2 + 5x - 2}{x}\right) = \frac{d}{dx}\left(3x + 5 - 2x^{-1}\right) = 3 + 2x^{-2}$$

The **chain rule** is used to differentiate **composite** functions. This is sometimes known as differentiating **a function of a function**. If y is a function of u, and u is a function of x, then $\dfrac{dy}{dx} = \dfrac{dy}{du} \times \dfrac{du}{dx}$.

For example, to differentiate $y = \left(3x^2 + 5\right)^8$, let $y = u^8$ where $u = 3x^2 + 5$, then

$$\frac{dy}{du} = 8u^7 \text{ and } \frac{du}{dx} = 6x \text{ so } \frac{dy}{dx} = 8u^7 \times 6x = 48x\left(3x^2 + 5\right)^7$$

This technique is used when differentiating **implicitly.**

Note that $\dfrac{d}{dx}\left(y^2\right) = \dfrac{d}{dy}\left(y^2\right)\dfrac{dy}{dx} = 2y\dfrac{dy}{dx}$, so if $y^2 + 3x^2 - y = 4x$,

then $2y\dfrac{dy}{dx} + 6x - \dfrac{dy}{dx} = 4 \Rightarrow \dfrac{dy}{dx} = \dfrac{4 - 6x}{2y - 1}$

You should be familiar with these **standard results**:

$$\frac{d}{dx}(\sin ax) = a \cos ax \qquad \frac{d}{dx}(e^{ax}) = ae^{ax} \qquad \frac{d}{dx}(\ln (ax+b)) = \frac{a}{ax+b}$$

$$\frac{d}{dx}(\cos ax) = -a \sin ax \qquad \frac{d}{dx}(e^{f(x)}) = f'(x)e^{f(x)} \quad \frac{d}{dx}(\ln f(x)) = \frac{f'(x)}{f(x)}$$

$$\frac{d}{dx}(\tan ax) = a \sec^2 ax$$

When expressions cannot be simplified, it may be necessary to use one of the following.

Product rule: **Quotient rule:**

$$\frac{d}{dx}(uv) = u\frac{dv}{dx} + v\frac{du}{dx} \qquad\qquad \frac{d}{dx}\left(\frac{u}{v}\right) = \frac{v\dfrac{du}{dx} - u\dfrac{dv}{dx}}{v^2}$$

If x and y are both functions of another variable, say t, then $\dfrac{dy}{dx} = \dfrac{dy}{dt} \times \dfrac{dt}{dx}$.
This is called **parametric differentiation**.

Note that $\dfrac{dt}{dx} = \dfrac{1}{dx/dt}$. For example, if $x = t^3$, $y = t^2$, then

$$\frac{dx}{dt} = 3t^2 \Rightarrow \frac{dt}{dx} = \frac{1}{3t^2} \; ; \; \frac{dy}{dt} = 2t; \text{ therefore } \frac{dy}{dx} = 2t \times \frac{1}{3t^2} = \frac{2}{3t}.$$

To find the **equation of the tangent** at $P(x_1, y_1)$ on a curve, find the value of $\dfrac{dy}{dx}$ at P.

Call this m, then use $y - y_1 = m(x - x_1)$. The gradient of the **normal** can be found from the

gradient of the tangent, remembering that for two perpendicular lines, $m_1 \times m_2 = -1$.

A **stationary point** is one where $\dfrac{dy}{dx} = 0$. It could be one of the following:

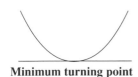   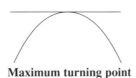   

Minimum turning point   **Maximum turning point**   **Stationary point of inflexion**

If you need to
revise this
subject more
thoroughly,
see the relevant
topics in the
Letts A level
Mathematics
Study Guide.

To investigate the nature of a stationary point, either

- Consider the value of y near the point.

- Look at the sign of $\dfrac{dy}{dx}$ either side of the point, noting the pattern of the gradient:

     Minimum   **Maximum**   **Points of inflexion with zero gradient**

- Consider the sign of the second differential $\dfrac{d}{dx}\left(\dfrac{dy}{dx}\right)$ written $\dfrac{d^2y}{dx^2}$.

If $\dfrac{dy}{dx} = 0$ and $\dfrac{d^2y}{dx^2} > 0$ there is a minimum turning point; if $\dfrac{dy}{dx} = 0$ and $\dfrac{d^2y}{dx^2} < 0$ there is a
maximum turning point. Note that if the second differential is zero, then no conclusions can be
drawn and one of the other methods must be used.

6 Differentiation

1   Differentiate the following functions with respect to x:

(a) $3e^{2x}$;   (1)

(b) $x^2 \cos x$;   (2)

(c) $\dfrac{\sin x}{x}$ (2)

Oxford

2   The radius r cm of a circular ink spot, t seconds after it first appears, is given by

$$r = \frac{1+4t}{2+t}.$$

Calculate

(a) the time taken for the radius to double its initial value;   (3)

(b) the rate of increase of the radius in cm s^{-1} when $t = 3$;   (5)

(c) the value to which r tends as t tends to infinity.   (2)

AEB

3   Find the equation of the tangent to the curve $y = (4x + 3)^5$ at the point $(-\frac{1}{2}, 1)$, giving your answer in the form $y = mx + c$.   (5)

UCLES

4   Use differentiation to find the coordinates of the stationary points on the curve

$$y = x + \frac{4}{x},$$

and determine whether each stationary point is a maximum point or a minimum point.   (5)

Find the set of values of x for which y increases as x increases.   (3)

UCLES

5   Find the gradient of the tangent to the parabola $y = 4x - x^2$ at $(0, 0)$.

Hence calculate the size of the angle between the line $y = x$ and this tangent.   (6)

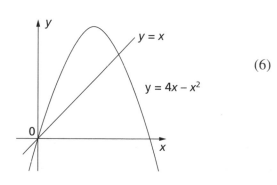

SEB

6   The parametric equations of a curve are

$$x = e^{2t} - 5t, \quad y = e^{2t} - 2t$$

Find $\dfrac{dy}{dx}$ in terms of t.   (3)

Find the exact value of t at the point on the curve where the gradient is 2.   (3)

UCLES

7 In a medical treatment 500 milligrammes of a drug are administered to a patient. At time t hours after the drug is administered X milligrammes of the drug remain in the patient. The doctor has a mathematical model which states that

$$X = 500\mathrm{e}^{-\frac{1}{5}t}.$$

(a) Find the value of t, correct to two decimal places, when $X = 200$. (3)

(b) (i) Express $\dfrac{\mathrm{d}X}{\mathrm{d}t}$ in terms of t. (2)

    (ii) Hence show that when $X = 200$ the rate of decrease of the amount of the drug remaining in the patient is 40 milligrammes per hour. (1)

NEAB

8 The graph of

$$y = x^3 + bx^2 + cx$$

is illustrated below.

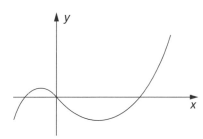

(a) Write down an expression for $\dfrac{\mathrm{d}y}{\mathrm{d}x}$. (2)

The curve has stationary points when $x = -1$ and $x = 3$.

(b) Show that $b = -3$ and calculate the value of c. (5)

(c) Hence find the local maximum and minimum values of y. (2)

(d) The graph is now translated by $\begin{pmatrix} 0 \\ d \end{pmatrix}$. Find the ranges of values for d such that the translated graph will have only one zero. (2)

NEAB (SMP 16–19)

9

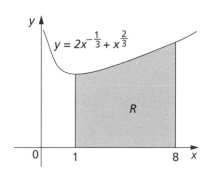

The figure shows a sketch of the curve with equation $y = 2x^{-\frac{1}{3}} + x^{\frac{2}{3}}$ for positive values of x.

(a) Find $\dfrac{\mathrm{d}y}{\mathrm{d}x}$ and hence show that at $x = 1$, $\dfrac{\mathrm{d}y}{\mathrm{d}x} = 0$.

The shaded region R is bounded by the curve, the x-axis and the lines $x = 1$ and $x = 8$.

(b) Determine the area of R. (12)

London Examinations

7 Integration

Integration can be thought of as the reverse process of differentiation. In order to integrate with confidence it is helpful to have a good knowledge of differentiation techniques, because when integrating a function, we often try to figure out what has been differentiated to give that function.

For **definite integration**, **limits** are given and a numerical value obtained. When there are no limits, the integration is known as **indefinite**, and it is necessary to include the **integration constant**, usually written c. To find the value of c, additional information is needed.

There are many **standard methods of integrating** and it is useful to adopt a systematic approach. Here are some techniques to consider:

For **powers of** x

when $n \neq -1$, $\int ax^n \, dx = \frac{a}{n+1} x^{n+1} + c$ and when $n = -1$, we have $\int \frac{a}{x} \, dx = a \ln|x| + c$.

Take care especially with negative and fractional indices when working out integrals.

The following integrals of **trigonometric functions** can be deduced from the differentials of $\sin ax$, $\cos ax$ and $\tan ax$, (see differentiation summary). Remember that angles are in radians.

$$\int \cos ax \, dx = \frac{1}{a} \sin ax + c \qquad \int \sin ax \, dx = -\frac{1}{a} \cos ax + c \qquad \int \sec^2 ax \, dx = \frac{1}{a} \tan ax + c$$

For example, $\int \left(3 \cos 2x - 4 \sec^2 3x\right) dx = \frac{3}{2} \sin 2x - \frac{4}{3} \tan 3x + c$.

We can now integrate trigonometrical functions which can be written in one of these formats, such as

$$\int_0^{\pi/4} \tan^2 x \, dx = \int_0^{\pi/4} \left(\sec^2 x - 1\right) dx = \left[\tan x - x\right]_0^{\pi/4} = 1 - \frac{\pi}{4}.$$

To integrate **even powers of cos** x **and sin** x use the double angle formula for cos, for example:

$$\int \sin^2 x \, dx = \int \frac{1}{2}(1 - \cos 2x) \, dx = \frac{1}{2}\left(x - \frac{1}{2} \sin 2x\right) + c$$

Consider whether a suitable **substitution** will help, for example to find

$$\int x(5x-3)^8 \, dx, \text{ let } 5x-3 = u \Rightarrow x = \frac{1}{5}(u+3), \frac{dx}{du} = \frac{1}{5},$$

and the integral becomes $\int \frac{1}{5}(u+3)u^8 \frac{1}{5} \, du = \frac{1}{25}\int \left(u^9 + 3u^8\right) du$.

For definite integrals, change the x limits to u limits when you make the substitution. If there are no limits, remember to change back to the original variable at the end.

Some integrals require a **trigonometric substitution**, for example, using $x = a \tan x$ we find that

$$\int \frac{1}{a^2 + x^2} \, dx = \frac{1}{a} \tan^{-1}\left(\frac{x}{a}\right) + c \text{ and using } x = a \sin x \text{ gives } \int \frac{1}{\sqrt{a^2 - x^2}} \, dx = \sin^{-1}\left(\frac{x}{a}\right) + c.$$

You can by-pass the substitution process if you **recognise an application of the chain rule**.

- $\dfrac{d}{dx}\left(x^4+2\right)^6 = 24x^3\left(x^4+2\right)^5 \Rightarrow \int x^3\left(x^4+2\right)^5 dx = \frac{1}{24}\left(x^4+2\right)^6 + c$

- $\dfrac{d}{dx}\left(e^{-3x+2}\right) = -3e^{-3x+2} \Rightarrow \int e^{-3x+2}dx = -\frac{1}{3}e^{-3x+2} + c$

- $\dfrac{d}{dx}\left(\sin^4 x\right) = 4\sin^3 x \cos x \Rightarrow \int 5\sin^3 x \cos x\, dx = \frac{5}{4}\sin^4 x + c$

The last example illustrates the technique needed to integrate **odd powers of cos x or sin x**, for example to integrate $\cos^3 x$ write it as $\cos x\left(1-\sin^2 x\right) = \cos x - \cos x \sin^2 x$ and it can then be integrated directly by recognition.

So when **integrating by recognition**, make a guess at the integral, and then check it by differentiating, correcting the numerical factor if necessary. Look particularly for integrals of the type $\int f'(x)\left[f(x)\right]^n dx$.

For integrals in **quotient form**, look for a fraction in which the numerator is the differential of the denominator. This indicates that the integral is a **logarithmic function**, where
$\int \dfrac{f'(x)}{f(x)}\, dx = \ln|f(x)| + c$. It is often necessary to adjust the numerical factor, for example,

$\int \dfrac{5x^2}{4x^3-1}\, dx = \frac{5}{12}\ln|4x^3-1| + c$ 	 	 $\int \tan x\, dx = \int \dfrac{\sin x}{\cos x}\, dx = -\ln|\cos x| + c = \ln|\sec x| + c$

Check whether the denominator can be factorised and the function written in **partial fractions**.

$\int \dfrac{x+13}{x^2+2x-15}\, dx = \int\left(\dfrac{2}{x-3} - \dfrac{1}{x+5}\right) dx = 2\ln|x-3| - \ln|x+5| + c.$

When integrating a **product**, check whether it can be simplified, recognised or integrated by use of a substitution. If not, consider **integration by parts**, remembering that sometimes it is necessary to perform the procedure more than once. The formula is complicated to write out, but is straightforward to use in practice:

$$\int u\dfrac{dv}{dx}\, dx = uv - \int v\dfrac{du}{dx}\, dx.$$

To find $\int x \cos 2x\, dx$, let $u = x \Rightarrow \dfrac{du}{dx} = 1$ and let $\dfrac{dv}{dx} = \cos 2x \Rightarrow v = \frac{1}{2}\sin 2x$.

Therefore $\int x \cos 2x\, dx = x\frac{1}{2}\sin 2x - \int \frac{1}{2}\sin 2x(1)\, dx = \frac{1}{2}x\sin 2x + \frac{1}{4}\cos 2x + c.$

When integrating products which involve a power of x it is usual to take this as u, but note this particular case: write $\int x^n \ln x\, dx$ as $\int \ln x\left(x^n\right) dx$. A special application of this enables us to integrate $\ln x$, where
$\int \ln x\, dx = \int \ln x \times 1\, dx = \ln x(x) - \int x\times\dfrac{1}{x}\, dx = x\ln x - x + c.$

An important application of integration is in finding **areas and volumes**.

To find the **area** between the curve, the x-axis and the lines $x = a$, $x = b$:

$$\text{Area} = \int_a^b y \, dx$$

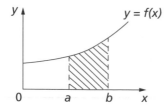

To find the **area** between the curve, the y-axis and the lines $y = c$, $y = d$:

$$\text{Area} = \int_c^d x \, dy$$

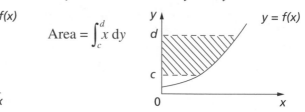

It is helpful to draw a sketch of the curve; this will enable you to spot any discontinuities. Remember also that some areas are negative and it may be necessary to integrate in sections.

The **area enclosed by two curves** is given by

$$\text{Area} = \int_{x_1}^{x_2} (y_1 - y_2) \, dx$$

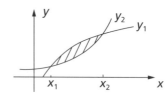

To find the **volume** obtained by rotating an area through one revolution:

About the x-axis: $\text{Volume} = \pi \int_a^b y^2 \, dx$

About the y-axis: $\text{Volume} = \pi \int_c^d x^2 \, dy$

You may be asked to form a **differential equation** from given information.

For example, if the rate of decay of m with t is proportional to m then $\dfrac{dm}{dt} \propto m$.

Since a rate of *decay* indicates a *negative* rate of change, we usually denote this by writing $\dfrac{dm}{dt} = -km$ with $k > 0$.

To find m, **separate the variables**, so

$$\int \frac{1}{m} \, dm = -\int k \, dt \ \Rightarrow \ \ln m = -kt + c. \qquad\qquad (|m| = m \text{ since } m > 0)$$

If you need to revise this subject more thoroughly, see the relevant topics in the *Letts* A level Mathematics Study Guide.

Additional information enables the value of c, the integration constant, to be found. For example, if $m = m_o$ when $t = 0$, then $\ln m_o = c$ so

$$\ln m = -kt + \ln m_o \ \Rightarrow \ \ln\left(\frac{m}{m_o}\right) = -kt \ \Rightarrow \ m = m_o e^{-kt}.$$

Note that further information is required in order to find k, the proportionality constant.

1 (i) Find

(a) $\int (2x + 3)^4 \, dx$,

(b) $\int \left(1 + \dfrac{3}{4x}\right) dx$. (5)

(ii) Find $\int 6\sqrt{x} \, dx$, and hence evaluate $\int_1^4 6\sqrt{x} \, dx$. (3)

UCLES

2 (a) Differentiate $\left(1 + x^3\right)^{\frac{1}{2}}$ with respect to x. (3)

(b) Use the result from (a), or an appropriate substitution, to find the value of

$$\int_0^2 \frac{x^2}{\sqrt{1 + x^3}} \, dx.$$ (4)

AEB

3 Curves C_1 and C_2 have equations $y = \dfrac{1}{x}$ and $y = kx^2$ respectively, where k is a constant.

The curves intersect at the point P, whose x-coordinate is $\frac{1}{2}$.

(a) Determine the value of k.

(b) Find the gradient of C_1 at P.

(c) Calculate the area of the finite region bounded by C_1, C_2, the x-axis and the line $x = 2$, giving your answer to 2 decimal places. (15)

London Examinations

4 (a) Sketch the area represented by the integral $\int_2^5 x^2 \, dx$ and calculate the value of the integral, showing your working. (2)

(b) Use your result from (a) to calculate the value of $\int_4^{25} \sqrt{y} \, dy$. (2)

Note that you will obtain no marks unless you use your result from (a).

(c) Calculate the volume obtained by revolving the part of the graph of $y = \sqrt{x + 1}$ between $x = 3$ and $x = 5$, through $360°$ around the x-axis, showing your working. (2)

Oxford (Nuffield)

5 (a) Differentiate $x \ln x$ with respect to x and hence show that the curve $y = x \ln x \ (x > 0)$ has a minimum point for $x = \frac{1}{e}$. State the corresponding y coordinate. (5)

(b) Give a reason why the curve has no point of inflection. (1)

(c) Sketch the curve for $x \geq \frac{1}{e}$. (1))

(d) Find the point A where the curve meets the line $y = x$ and find the area enclosed by the line OA, the curve and the x-axis. (5)

NEAB

6 Find

(a) $\int x \cos x \, \mathrm{d}x$,

(b) $\int \cos^2 y \, \mathrm{d}y$.

Hence find the general solution of the differential equation

$$\frac{\mathrm{d}y}{\mathrm{d}x} = x \cos x \sec^2 2y, \quad 0 < y < \frac{\pi}{4}.$$

(12)
London Examinations

7 Radium is a radioactive substance. You can model its decay by the differential equation
$\frac{\mathrm{d}R}{\mathrm{d}t} = -kR$ where t is the time in years, R is the amount of radium in grams present at time t,
and k is a positive constant.

Suppose that when $t = 0$, 10 g of radium is present.

(a) Solve the equation $\frac{\mathrm{d}R}{\mathrm{d}t} = -kR$ to find R in terms of t and k. (2)

(b) It is known that the amount of radium will have halved after about 1600 years. Use this
information to show that $k = \frac{\ln 2}{1600}$. (2)

(c) According to this model, how many grams of radium will be left after 100 years? (2)
Oxford (Nuffield)

8 A circular patch of oil on the surface of water has radius r metres at time t minutes.
When $t = 0$, $r = 1$ and when $t = 10$, $r = 2$. It is desired to predict the value T of t when $r = 4$.

(i) In a simple model the rate of increase of r is taken to be a constant. Find T for this
model. (3)

(ii) In a more refined model, the rate of increase of r is taken to be proportional to $\frac{1}{r}$.

Express this statement as a differential equation, and find the general solution. (4)

Find T for this second model. (4)
UCLES

9 Use the substitution $x = 2 \cos \theta$ or otherwise, to evaluate

$$\int_1^{\sqrt{2}} \frac{1}{x^2 \sqrt{4 - x^2}} \, \mathrm{d}x$$

giving your answer in surd form. (5)
Oxford

10 Given that $\frac{\mathrm{d}^2 y}{\mathrm{d}x^2} = 4$, find y in terms of x if $y = 3$ when $x = 0$ and $y = 5$ when $x = 2$. (4)
Oxford

11 The curve C is given by the equations

$$x = 2t, \; y = t^2,$$

where t is a parameter.

(a) Find an equation of the normal to C at the point P on C where $t = 3$.

The normal meets the y-axis at the point B. The finite region R is bounded by the part of the curve C between the origin O and P, and the lines OB and BP.

(b) Show the region R, together with its boundaries, in a sketch.

The region R is rotated through 2π about the y-axis to form a solid S.

(c) Using integration, and explaining each step in your method, find the volume of S, giving your answer in terms of π. (17)

London Examinations

12 A particle is moving in a straight line and its velocity, v m s^{-1}, t seconds after passing a fixed point O is given by

$$v = 3t^2 + 1$$

(a) Find the acceleration of the particle when $t = 4$. (2)

(b) Determine the displacement from O when $t = 4$. (3)

Oxford

13 It is given that, for $0 \le x \le 0.2$, the curve $y = \ln (1 + x)$ can be closely approximated by the curve $y = x - \frac{1}{2}x^2$. For each of these curves find $\dfrac{dy}{dx}$. Hence find the gradient of each curve when $x = 0.2$. (3)

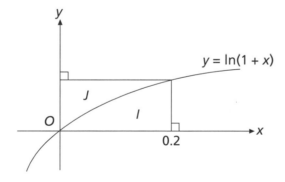

The diagram shows the curve $y = \ln (1 + x)$. The region bounded by the curve, the x-axis and the line $x = 0.2$ is denoted by I.

(i) Find an approximation to the area of I by evaluating

$$\int_0^{0.2} (x - \tfrac{1}{2}x^2) \, dx,$$

giving the answer correct to 4 decimal places. (2)

(ii) Rearrange $y = \ln (1 + x)$ to express x in terms of y. (2)

Hence find the exact area of the region J shown in the diagram. (3)

Deduce the area of the region I, giving the answer correct to 4 decimal places. (2)

UCLES

8 _Numerical methods_

Numerical methods provide us with an alternative approach to solving equations that may be difficult, or impossible, to solve algebraically. The use of graphics calculators, in particular, enables us to apply these methods with great efficiency.

Consider the equation $e^x - 4x - 3 = 0$. Sketching the graph of $y = e^x - 4x - 3$ provides important information about the nature of the solutions and their approximate values.

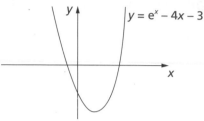

The **trace** function of a graphics calculator reveals the approximate solutions as –0.6 and 2.6.

Numerical methods may now be employed to refine these estimates to a high degree of accuracy.

Taking $f(x) = e^x - 4x - 3$, a **systematic search** is carried out by evaluating $f(x)$ at points near to a root, and looking for a change of sign. In this case, for example, $f(2.5) = -0.8... < 0$ and $f(2.6) = 0.06... > 0$, which tells us that the solution lies between 2.5 and 2.6. The table below shows how the process may be continued. The same approach is used to find the root near –0.6.

$x : f(x) < 0$	$x : f(x) > 0$	Solution in interval
2.5	2.6	(2.5, 2.6)
2.58		(2.58, 2.6)
2.59		(2.59, 2.6)
	2.595	(2.59, 2.595)
	2.594	(2.59, 2.594)
2.593		(2.593, 2.594)
	2.5935	(2.593, 2.5935)

A graphics calculator key sequence such as

$? \to X : e^x - 4X - 3$

allows $f(x)$ to be calculated, for different trial values, with the minimum of effort.

Since it has now been established that a root lies between 2.593 and 2.5935 it follows that its value may now be stated as 2.593 correct to 3 decimal places.

In essence, the **interval bisection** method is the same as the systematic search except that, at each stage, $f(x)$ is evaluated at the mid-point of the interval in which the root is known to lie.

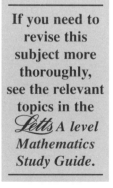

**If you need to
revise this
subject more
thoroughly,
see the relevant
topics in the
Letts A level
Mathematics
Study Guide.**

The equation $e^x - 4x - 3 = 0$ can be rearranged as $x = \dfrac{e^x - 3}{4}$ to give the **iteration** formula $x_{n+1} = \dfrac{e^{x_n} - 3}{4}$.

The graph illustrates the effect of using this iteration formula from different starting points. The iteration always _fails_ to converge to the upper root. However, it will converge to the lower root from any starting point less than the upper root.

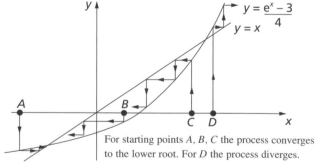

For starting points A, B, C the process converges to the lower root. For D the process diverges.

A different rearrangement of the original equation produces the iteration formula $x_{n+1} = \ln(4x_n + 3)$, which converges to the upper root from any starting point greater than the lower root. It follows that this re-arrangement fails to converge to the lower root.

Another fixed point iterative method, for the solution of $f(x) = 0$, is the **Newton-Raphson**

method given by $x_{n+1} = x_n - \dfrac{f(x_n)}{f'(x_n)}$. For the given equation, this gives $x_{n+1} = x_n - \dfrac{e^{x_n} - 4x_n - 3}{e^{x_n} - 4}$ which can converge rapidly to _both_ roots depending on the starting value.

1 The sequence given by the iteration formula
$$x_{n+1} = 2(1 + e^{-x_n}),$$

with $x_1 = 0$, converges to α. Find α correct to 3 decimal places, and state an equation of which α is a root. (4)

UCLES

2 (a) Show that the equation $x^3 + 3x^2 - 7 = 0$ may be rearranged into the form $x = \sqrt{\dfrac{a}{x+b}}$, and state the values of a and b.

(b) Hence, using the iteration formula
$$x_{n+1} = \sqrt{\frac{a}{x_n + b}}$$

with $x_0 = 2$ together with your values of a and b, find the approximate solution x_4 of the equation, giving your answer to an appropriate degree of accuracy. Show your intermediate answers and explain why the degree of accuracy you have chosen for x_4 is appropriate. (7)

London Examinations

3 Show that the equation $x^3 - x^2 - 2 = 0$ has a root α which lies between 1 and 2. (2)

(a) Using 1.5 as a first approximation for α, use the Newton-Raphson method once to obtain a second approximation for α, giving your answer to 3 decimal places. (4)

(b) Show that the equation $x^3 - x^2 - 2 = 0$ can be arranged in the form $x = \sqrt[3]{(f(x))}$ where $f(x)$ is a quadratic function.

Use an iteration of the form $x_{n+1} = g(x_n)$ based on this rearrangement and with $x_1 = 1.5$ to find x_2 and x_3, giving your answers to 3 decimal places. (5)

AEB

4 The function f is defined by
$$f(x) = e^x - 5x, \quad x \in \mathbb{R}$$

(a) Determine $f'(x)$.

(b) Find the value of x for which $f'(x) = 0$ giving your answer to 2 decimal places.

(c) Show, by calculation, that there is a root α of the equation $f(x) = 0$ such that $0.2 < \alpha < 0.3$.

(d) Determine the integer p such that the other root β of the equation $f(x) = 0$ lies in the interval
$$\frac{p}{10} < \beta < \frac{p+1}{10}.$$
(12)

London Examinations

5 (a) By sketching the curves with equations $y = 4 - x^2$ and $y = e^x$, show that the equation $x^2 + e^x - 4 = 0$ has one negative root and one positive root.

(b) Use the iteration formula $x_{n+1} = -(4 - e^{x_n})^{1/2}$ with $x_0 = -2$ to find in turn x_1, x_2, x_3 and x_4 and hence write down an approximation to the negative root of the equation, giving your answer to 4 decimal places.

An attempt to evaluate the positive root of the equation is made using the iteration formula $x_{n+1} = (4 - e^{x_n})^{1/2}$ with $x_0 = 1.3$.

(c) Describe the result of such an attempt. (11)

London Examinations

6 On a single diagram, sketch the graphs of $y = \ln(10x)$ and $y = \dfrac{6}{x}$, and explain how you can deduce that the equation $\ln(10x) = \dfrac{6}{x}$ has exactly one real root. (3)

Given that the root is close to 2, use the iteration

$$x_{n+1} = \frac{6}{\ln(10x_n)}$$

to evaluate the root correct to three decimal places. (2)

The same equation may be written in the form $x\ln(10x) - 6 = 0$. Taking $f(x)$ to be $x\ln(10x) - 6$, find $f'(x)$, and show that the Newton-Raphson iteration for the root of $f(x) = 0$ may be simplified to the form

$$x_{n+1} = \frac{x_n + 6}{1 + \ln(10x_n)}.$$

(5)

UCLES

7 The chord AB of a circle subtends an angle θ radians at the centre O of the circle of radius r, as shown in the diagram.

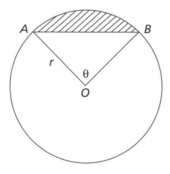

(a) Find an expression for the shaded area, in terms of r and θ. (3)

(b) Given that this shaded area is $\frac{1}{6}$ of the area of the circle, show that θ is given by

$$\sin\theta = \theta - \frac{\pi}{3}.$$

(1)

(c) By sketching the graphs of $y = \sin\theta$ and $y = \theta - \dfrac{\pi}{3}$ on the same diagram, verify that

$\theta = 2$ is an approximate solution of the equation $\sin\theta = \theta - \dfrac{\pi}{3}$. (2)

(d) Find a better approximation for θ using one application of Newton's rule. (3)

NEAB

Mathematics of uncertainty 9

When asked to suggest suitable ways of **collecting data**, bear in mind the purpose for which they are to be used and how best to **organise** them so that they will be easy to assimilate and interpret. You should be familiar with **methods of presentation** such as pie charts, histograms, frequency graphs, cumulative frequency graphs and scatter diagrams. You may be asked to discuss advantages and/or disadvantages of particular representations.

In a **histogram**, the area of a bar represents the frequency. Problems arise when intervals are of unequal widths, in which case it is easiest to use the **frequency density** of an interval as the height of the bar, where frequency density $= \dfrac{\text{frequency}}{\text{interval width}}$. A **frequency graph** is formed by plotting the frequency density against the **mid-points** of the intervals and joining the points with straight lines (frequency polygon) or a smooth curve.

Cumulative frequency represents a running total, and when drawing **cumulative frequency graphs**, remember to plot the cumulative frequency against the **upper class boundary** of an interval.

The measures of **central tendency** (sometimes called measures of location) are the three **averages**: mode, mean and median. For raw data, the **mode** is the value that occurs most often. When data have been grouped, the **modal class** is the one with the greatest frequency density. The **mean** is the arithmetic average and it takes account of every reading. Often you will use the statistical functions on your calculator, but you should be familiar with the formulae for the mean, remembering that for grouped data, the mid-point of the interval is used for x.

For raw data, $\bar{x} = \dfrac{\sum x}{n}$ and for data in a frequency distribution, $\bar{x} = \dfrac{\sum fx}{\sum f}$.

The **median** is the middle value when the data are arranged in order; for grouped data, find the $\frac{1}{2}n$th value either from a cumulative frequency curve or by **linear interpolation**. The median is a useful average, especially when the distribution contains extreme values.

The **standard deviation** gives a useful **measure of dispersion**, or **spread**, because it takes account of every reading. Note that in most distributions the bulk of the readings lie within two standard deviations of the mean. You will probably use your calculator to find it, but make sure that you can use the formula if necessary, where $s = \sqrt{\dfrac{\sum f(x-\bar{x})^2}{\sum f}}$ or $s = \sqrt{\dfrac{\sum fx^2}{\sum f} - \bar{x}^2}$.

Other measures of spread include the complete **range** (the difference between the highest and lowest readings) and the range of the middle half of the readings, known as the **interquartile range**. This is given by the difference between the upper quartile and the lower quartile, where the upper quartile is the $\frac{3}{4}n$th value and the lower quartile is the $\frac{1}{4}n$th value. A concise way of representing both of these ranges is on a **box and whisker diagram**, from which it is easy to assess the **skewness** of the distribution.

Probability: Two events, A and B, are **mutually exclusive** if the occurrence of one of them excludes the occurrence of the other, in which case $P(A \text{ or } B) = P(A) + P(B)$.

Two events, A and B, are **independent** if the outcome of one event does not affect the outcome of the other, in which case $P(A \text{ and } B) = P(A) \times P(B)$.

These two formulae are special cases of the following rules for **any two events**, A and B:
   (i) $P(A \text{ or } B) = P(A) + P(B) - P(A \text{ and } B)$, where $P(A \text{ or } B)$ means $P(A \text{ or } B \text{ or both})$;
   (ii) $P(A \text{ and } B) = P(A) \times P(B|A)$, where $P(B|A)$ is the **conditional probability** that B occurs, given that A occurs. Note that when the events are independent, $P(B|A) = P(B)$.

When finding probabilities, it is often helpful to use **possibility spaces** or **tree diagrams**.

If you need to revise this subject more thoroughly, see the relevant topics in the *Letts* A level Mathematics Study Guide.

1   An angler made a record of the weights (in lb) of the 200 fish he caught during one year. These are summarised in the table.

Weight of fish, lb (mid-class value)	0.5	1.25	1.75	2.25	2.75	3.5	4.5	5.5	7.0	10.5
Number of fish in the class	21	32	33	24	18	21	16	12	11	12
Class width	1	0.5	0.5	0.5	0.5	1	1	1	2	5

Using the information supplied in the table:

(a) calculate suitable frequency densities and, on graph paper, construct a histogram of the data;   (4)

(b) calculate estimates of the mean and standard deviation of the weights of the fish.   (3)

Oxford

2   The distribution of speeds of a sample of 250 vehicles on an inner city road is summarised in the following table. The road is subject to a 30 mph speed limit.

Speed, v, in mph	Number of vehicles
$10 < v \le 20$	18
$20 < v \le 25$	26
$25 < v \le 30$	90
$30 < v \le 35$	58
$35 < v \le 40$	32
$40 < v \le 50$	18
$50 < v \le 70$	8

(a) (i) Represent these data by a cumulative frequency diagram   (5)

   (ii) Estimate the median, lower quartile and upper quartile speeds of the vehicles.   (3)

(b) (i) Use your estimates obtained in part (a) to draw an approximate box plot.   (2)

   (ii) Comment briefly on the extent to which vehicles break the speed limit based on the evidence of this diagram.   (2)

NEAB

3 The following information appears in the Annual Report 1992 of Eurotunnel PLC.

Size of shareholding		Number of shareholders
1 –	99	133 853
100 –	499	347 495
500 –	999	79 087
1 000 –	1 499	31 638
1 500 –	2 499	27 547
2 500 –	4 999	10 655
5 000 –	9 999	3 842
10 000 –	49 999	2 188
50 000 –	99 999	283
100 000 –	249 999	216
250 000 –	499 999	82
500 000 –	999 999	54
1 000 000 and over		50
Total		636 990

(i) Explain briefly what difficulties would arise in attempting to

    (a) represent the data by means of an accurate and easily comprehensible diagram,   (2)

    (b) find the mean size of shareholding per shareholder.   (1)

(ii) Estimate the median size of shareholding.   (3)

UCLES

4 Two events A and B are such that $p(A) = 0.4$, $p(B) = 0.7$, $p(A \text{ or } B) = 0.8$.

Calculate

(a) $p(A \text{ and } B)$;   (2)

(b) the conditional probability $p(A|B)$.   (2)

AEB

5 Doctors estimate that three people in every thousand of the population are infected by a particular virus. A test has been devised which is not perfect, but gives a positive result for 95% of those who have the virus. It also gives a positive result for 2% of those who do not have the virus.

Suppose that someone selected at random takes the test and that it gives a positive result. Calculate the probability that this person really has the virus.   (8)

Oxford (Nuffield)

6 A bag contains 10 balls, of which 4 are red and 6 are blue. An experiment consists of drawing at random and without replacement 3 balls, one at a time, from the bag.

(a) Draw a tree diagram to show all the possible outcomes of the experiment.

Hence or otherwise, find the probability that

(b) the first 2 balls drawn will be of different colours,

(c) the third ball will be red,

(d) the third ball will be red, given that the first 2 balls drawn were both blue.   (11)

London Examinations

7 The following table gives a grouped frequency distribution of the heights of boys entering a certain school.

Height (h cm)	Frequency
$75 < h \leq 85$	7
$85 < h \leq 90$	32
$90 < h \leq 95$	55
$95 < h \leq 100$	47
$100 < h \leq 105$	33
$105 < h \leq 110$	18
$110 < h \leq 120$	8

(a) Calculate estimates of the mean and standard deviation of this distribution. (4)

(b) Draw a histogram on graph paper. (4)

WJEC

8 Computer chips are difficult to manufacture, and need to be checked for faults before they can be used. A test procedure has two stages, and in each stage the probability of a faulty chip failing is 0.9. Any chip that fails the first stage is immediately rejected and does not go through the second stage of the test. Chips with no faults always pass both stages of the test. The probability of any randomly chosen chip being faulty is 0.4. This information is illustrated in the following tree diagram.

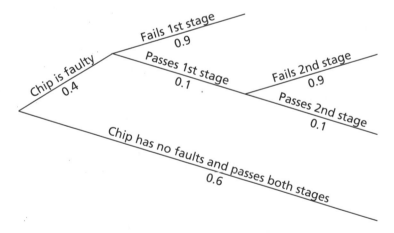

(i) Find the probability that a randomly chosen chip is faulty and passes both stages of the test. (2)

(ii) Find the probability that a randomly chosen chip passes both stages of the test. (2)

(iii) Find the conditional probability that a randomly chosen chip is faulty, given that it passes both stages of the test. (2)

UCLES

9

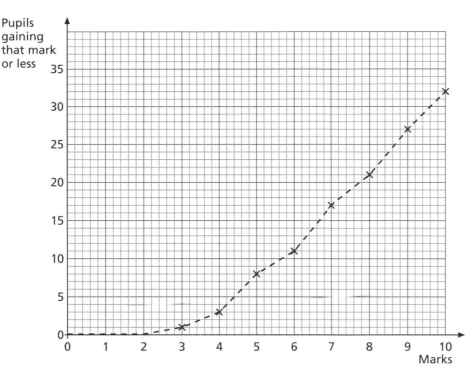

The diagram is a *cumulative* frequency graph showing the number of pupils in a class who gained the plotted mark *or less* in a test. The maximum mark for the test was 10.

(i) How many children gained (a) 5 marks or less, (b) exactly 5 marks? (2)

(ii) Compile a frequency table for this distribution. (3)

(iii)Calculate the mean and the standard deviation of the pupils' marks. (3)

Oxford & Cambridge

10 Vectors

REVISION
SUMMARY

Vector addition and subtraction

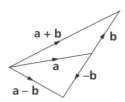

Multiplication by a scalar

In the usual notation, the letter O is used to denote the position of some fixed reference point called the **origin**. If P is some other point, then the vector from O to P (written as $\overrightarrow{OP}$ or **OP**) is referred to as the **position vector** of P.

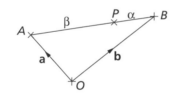

$\overrightarrow{AB} = \mathbf{b} - \mathbf{a}$

The position vector of a point dividing a line in a given ratio is given by

$$\overrightarrow{OP} = \frac{\alpha\mathbf{a} + \beta\mathbf{b}}{\alpha + \beta}$$

The **vector equation of a line** is in the form $\mathbf{r} = \mathbf{a} + t\mathbf{b}$ where **a** is the position vector of some fixed point on the line, **b** is a constant vector parallel to the line (often described as the direction vector) and t is a scalar parameter. As t changes, **r** represents the general position vector of a point on the line.

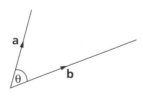

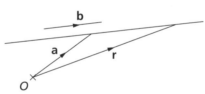

If the coordinates of P are (x, y, z) then the position vector $\overrightarrow{OP}$ may be written as $\begin{pmatrix} x \\ y \\ z \end{pmatrix}$ or as $x\mathbf{i} + y\mathbf{j} + z\mathbf{k}$.

If you need to revise this subject more thoroughly, see the relevant topics in the *Letts* A level *Mathematics Study Guide*.

The distance OP is given by the **magnitude** of $\overrightarrow{OP}$ which is $\left|\overrightarrow{OP}\right| = \sqrt{x^2 + y^2 + z^2}$.

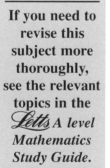

$\mathbf{a.b} = |\mathbf{a}||\mathbf{b}|\cos\theta$

The **scalar product a.b** is so-called because its value is a scalar. It is also known as the **dot product** because of the notation used.

(Note that $\mathbf{a} \times \mathbf{b}$ represents a *different* form of product in which the result is a vector).

A *very important* special case is that if **a** and **b** are perpendicular then $\mathbf{a.b} = 0$. For example $\mathbf{i.j} = \mathbf{i.k} = \mathbf{j.k} = 0$. Note also that $\mathbf{i.i} = 1$, $\mathbf{j.j} = 1$, $\mathbf{k.k} = 1$. These results may be used to establish a very simple method of calculating $\mathbf{a.b}$ when **a** and **b** are in component form.
If $\mathbf{a} = a_1\mathbf{i} + a_2\mathbf{j} + a_3\mathbf{k}$ and $\mathbf{b} = b_1\mathbf{i} + b_2\mathbf{j} + b_3\mathbf{k}$ then $\mathbf{a.b} = a_1b_1 + a_2b_2 + a_3b_3$.

The angle between two vectors may then be given by $\theta = \cos^{-1}\left(\dfrac{\mathbf{a.b}}{|\mathbf{a}||\mathbf{b}|}\right)$. To find the angle between two lines, find the angle between their direction vectors.

1 The vectors **a**, **b** and **c** are defined as follows:

$$\mathbf{a} = 2\mathbf{i} - \mathbf{k}, \quad \mathbf{b} = \mathbf{i} + 2\mathbf{j} + \mathbf{k}, \quad \mathbf{c} = -\mathbf{j} + \mathbf{k}.$$

(a) Evaluate **a.b** + **a.c**. (3)

(b) From your answer to part (a), make a deduction about the vector **b** + **c**. (2)

SEB

2

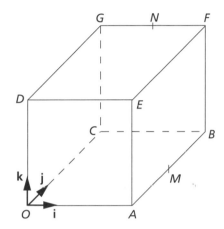

In the diagram *OABCDEFG* is a cube in which the length of each edge is 2 units. Unit

vectors **i**, **j**, **k** are parallel to $\overrightarrow{OA}, \overrightarrow{OC}, \overrightarrow{OD}$ respectively. The mid-points of *AB* and *FG* are *M* and *N* respectively.

(i) Express each of the vectors $\overrightarrow{ON}$ and $\overrightarrow{MG}$ in terms of **i**, **j** and **k**. (3)

(ii) Show that the acute angle between the directions of $\overrightarrow{ON}$ and $\overrightarrow{MG}$ is 63.6°, correct to the nearest 0.1°. (5)

UCLES

3 Vectors **r** and **s** are given by

$\mathbf{r} = \lambda\mathbf{i} + (2\lambda - 1)\mathbf{j} - \mathbf{k},$

$\mathbf{s} = (1 - \lambda)\mathbf{i} + 3\lambda\mathbf{j} + (4\lambda - 1)\mathbf{k},$

where λ is a scalar.

(a) Find the values of λ for which **r** and **s** are perpendicular.

When $\lambda = 2$, **r** and **s** are the position vectors of the points *A* and *B* respectively, referred to an origin *O*.

(b) Find $\overrightarrow{AB}$.

(c) Use a scalar product to find the size of angle *BAO*, giving your answer to the nearest degree. (14)

London Examinations

4 The line *l* has vector equation $\mathbf{r} = 2\mathbf{i} + s(\mathbf{i} + 3\mathbf{j} + 4\mathbf{k})$.

  (a) (i) Show that the line *l* intersects the line with equation $\mathbf{r} = \mathbf{k} + t(\mathbf{i} + \mathbf{j} + \mathbf{k})$ and
determine the position vector of the point of intersection.   (5)

   (ii) Calculate the acute angle, to the nearest degree, between these two lines.   (4)

  (b) Find the position vectors of the points on *l* which are exactly $5\sqrt{10}$ units from the
origin.   (5)

  (c) Determine the position vector of the point on *l* which is closest to the point with position
vector $6\mathbf{i} - \mathbf{j} + 3\mathbf{k}$.   (6)

Oxford

5 (a)

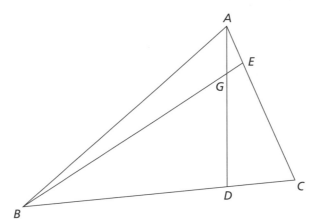

The points *A*, *B*, *C*, have position vectors **a**, **b**, **c** relative to an origin *O*. The points *D*, *E*
lie on *BC*, *CA* respectively such that $BD : DC = 2 : 1$ and $CE : EA = 3 : 1$. The lines *AD*
and *BE* meet at *G*.

  (i) Find the position vectors of D and E.

  (ii) Show that the position vector of *G* is

$$\frac{2}{3}\mathbf{a} + \frac{1}{9}\mathbf{b} + \frac{2}{9}\mathbf{c}.$$

  (iii) The line *CG* meets *AB* at *F*. Find the position vector of *F* in terms of **a** and **b**.   (10)

  (b) *OPQR* is a parallelogram and $\mathbf{OP} = \mathbf{p}$, $\mathbf{OR} = \mathbf{r}$.

  (i) Write down expressions in terms of **p** and **r** for **OQ** and **PR**.

  (ii) Given that $OP = OR$, show by considering the scalar product of **OQ** and **PR** that *OQ*
and *PR* are perpendicular.   (5)

WJEC

Answers

1 ALGEBRA

Answer	Mark	Examiner's tip

1 (i) $a^k = \sqrt[3]{(a)^4} \div a$

$a^k = a^{\frac{4}{3}} \div a^1$ — 2 — Apply the laws of indices to express the RHS of the equation in the same form as the LHS.

$a^k = a^{\frac{1}{3}}$

$\underline{k = \frac{1}{3}}$ — 2 — The indices may now be compared directly.

(ii) $27^x = 9^{(x-1)}$

$(3^3)^x = (3^2)^{(x-1)}$ — 2 — In essence, this is similar to part (i) but, this time, it is helpful to re-write both sides using the same number as base.

$3x = 2(x-1)$

$\underline{x = -2}$ — 2

2 (a) $2x^{\frac{1}{3}} = x^{-\frac{2}{3}}$

$2x = 1$ — 3 — The rational index is at the heart of this problem. A good first move is to multiply both sides of the equation

$\underline{x = \frac{1}{2}}$ — 1 — by $x^{\frac{2}{3}}$ which has the effect of clearing the fractions.

(b) $3^y = 6$

$y\ln 3 = \ln 6$ — 2 — Taking logs of both sides converts the equation to linear form.

$\underline{y = 1.63}$ (correct to 3 s.f.) — 3 — State the answer to the required degree of accuracy.

3 $y = a(b^x)$

$\ln y = \ln(ab^x)$

$\ln y = \ln a + x\ln b$ — 1 — The hint contained in the question is that we should take the natural logarithm of both sides to convert the equation to gradient-intercept form.

The gradient is given by $\ln b = 1.8$

$\Rightarrow \underline{b = e^{1.8} = 6.05}$ (to 3 s.f.) — 2

and the y-intercept is given by

$\ln a = 4.1$

$\Rightarrow \underline{a = e^{4.1} = 60.3}$ (to 3 s.f.) — 2

4 (i) (A) The population *increases* each year — 1

(B) The population *doesn't change* — 1

(C) The population *reduces* each year. — 1

(ii)

Year	1910	1920	1930	1940	1950	1960
n	10	20	30	40	50	60
$\log_{10}P_n$	1.57	1.64	1.72	1.81	1.89	1.97

— 2

Answer	Mark	Examiner's tip

(iii) For both marks you would have to plot all of the points accurately on the axes provided. **2**

(iv) Your answer should make reference to the fact that the graph is a straight line. **2**

Examiner's tip: Care should be taken to draw an accurate graph, because the readings taken from it later will be needed in calculations to check the model, $\log_{10} P_n = \log_{10} P_0 + n\log_{10} k$ which is in linear form, and so the model predicts that the graph of $\log_{10} P_n$ against n should be linear.

(v) From the graph, the y-intercept is given by $\log_{10} P_0 = 1.49 \Rightarrow \underline{P_0 = 31}$ (million, to nearest million)

and $\log_{10} k = 0.008 \Rightarrow \underline{k = 1.0186}$ (correct to 5 s.f.) **3**

Examiner's tip: Any greater accuracy couldn't be justified, based on the accuracy of the given data.

This is a high degree of accuracy, but it fits the given data very well.

(vi) Using the figures for P_0 and k from (v) in the model, there is close agreement with the actual figures. However, the predictions for 1970, 1980 and 1990 are far too high, which suggests that the pattern of population growth has changed. **2**

Examiner's tip: There is no need to go into too much detail - be guided by the number of marks available.

5 Let $f(x) = x^3 + ax^2 + bx - 4$

then $f(2) = 0 \Rightarrow 8 + 4a + 2b - 4 = 0$

$\Rightarrow 4a + 2b + 4 = 0$

$\Rightarrow 2a + b + 2 = 0$ (1) **1**

and $f(-2) = 0 \Rightarrow -8 + 4a - 2b - 4 = 0$

$\Rightarrow 2a - b - 6 = 0$ (2) **1**

(1) + (2) gives $4a - 4 = 0 \Rightarrow \underline{a = 1}$ **1**

Substituting for a in (1) gives $\underline{b = -4}$ **1**

Substituting for a and b in the original equation gives $x^3 + x^2 - 4x - 4 = (x - 2)(x + 2)g(x)$ (where $g(x)$ is linear).

i.e. $x^3 + x^2 - 4x - 4 = (x^2 - 4)g(x)$

and so $g(x) = \underline{x + 1}$ is the required linear factor. **2**

Examiner's tip: Consider introducing function notation as a means of making your method clear.

Check that $f(-1) = 0$.

6 (a) $f(-2) = 2(-2)^3 - 3(-2)^2 - 11(-2) + 6$

$= -16 - 12 + 22 + 6 = 0.$

$\therefore$ By the factor theorem $(x + 2)$ is a factor of $f(x)$. **1**

Examiner's tip: It's important to show some working – don't simply state that $f(-2) = 0$.
Make a point of referring to the factor theorem.

(b) $f(x) = (x + 2)(2x^2 - 7x + 3)$

$= \underline{(x + 2)(2x - 1)(x - 3)}$ **2**

Answer	Mark	Examiner's tip

(c)

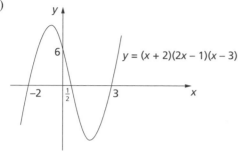

From the graph,
$f(x) \leq 0 \Rightarrow x \leq -2$ or $\frac{1}{2} \leq x \leq 3$.

2

The inequality, $f(x) \leq 0$, is solved by considering where the graph of the function lies on or below the x-axis.

There are only two marks available here so just a quick sketch showing the general shape and the points of intersection with the x-axis will suffice.

7 $x^2 - 4x + 9 = (x - 2)^2 - 4 + 9$
$\qquad\qquad\quad = (x - 2)^2 + 5$

2

Minimum value of $x^2 - 4x + 9$ is 5 and so the maximum value of $f(x)$ is $\frac{1}{5}$.

1

This result can be checked by using a graphics calculator to draw the graph of $y = f(x)$ and locating the maximum value with the trace function.

8 Let $f(x) = 2x^3 + ax^2 + 16x + 6$

then $f(x) = (2x + 1)g(x)$ where $g(x)$ is a polynomial function.

It follows that $f(-\frac{1}{2}) = 0$

i.e. $2(-\frac{1}{2})^3 + a(-\frac{1}{2})^2 + 16(-\frac{1}{2}) + 6 = 0$

1

$\Rightarrow -\frac{1}{4} + \frac{a}{4} - 8 + 6 = 0 \Rightarrow -1 + a - 8 = 0$
$\Rightarrow \underline{a = 9}$

1

$f(x) = (2x + 1)(x^2 + 4x + 6)$

i.e. the required quadratic factor is $x^2 + 4x + 6$.
Now, $x^2 + 4x + 6 = (x + 2)^2 - 4 + 6$
$\qquad\qquad\qquad = (x + 2)^2 + 2$

2

which is positive for all real values of x (the minimum value is 2).

2

The introduction of function notation can, again, make the task of filling in the necessary steps, to justify the end result, easier.

Having completed the square, some justification for concluding that the quadratic is always positive should be given. One way is to interpret the result in terms of the minimum value.

9 (i)

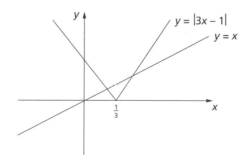

3

The graph of $y = |3x - 1|$ is the same as the graph of $y = 3x - 1$ wherever $3x - 1 \geq 0$, and corresponds to the graph of $y = -(3x - 1)$ when $3x - 1 < 0$.

(ii) The larger value of x corresponds to the solution of $3x - 1 = x$ (since at this point $3x - 1 > 0$).

$\Rightarrow x = \frac{1}{2}$

It is important to recognise how the modulus function behaves in order to produce **two** equations to be solved.

Answer	Mark	Examiner's tip

The smaller value of x corresponds to the solution of $-(3x - 1) = x$
(since at this point $3x - 1 < 0$).
$$\Rightarrow x = \tfrac{1}{4}$$

3

(iii) $|3x - 1| > x \Rightarrow x < \tfrac{1}{4}$ or $x > \tfrac{1}{2}$

3

The solutions occur where the graph of $y = |3x - 1|$ lies above the graph of $y = x$.

10 (a)

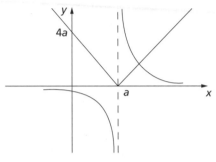

Take care to show the asymptotes clearly and to label the axes as specified in the question.

6

(b) Graphs intersect when $\dfrac{1}{x - a} = 4|x - a|$.

However, at point of intersection $x - a > 0$.

$$\Rightarrow \frac{1}{x - a} = 4(x - a)$$ **1**

$$\Rightarrow 1 = 4(x - a)^2$$

$$\Rightarrow x - a = \tfrac{1}{2} \text{ (positive solution only)}$$ **1**

$$\Rightarrow x = a + \tfrac{1}{2}$$ **1**

Give a brief explanation to make your method clear and to justify replacing $|x - a|$ with $(x - a)$ in the equation to be solved.

From the graph, the solutions of

$\dfrac{1}{x - a} < 4|x - a|$ are given by $x < a$ and

$x > a + \tfrac{1}{2}$. **3**

Use the graph to make sure that you identify *all* of the solutions.

11 $2x^2 + 4x + k = 0$

For real roots, the discriminant ≥ 0. **1**

Thus, $16 - 4 \times 2 \times k \geq 0$

i.e. $16 - 8k \geq 0$

giving $k \leq 2$. **1**

Make a clear statement about the significance of the discriminant.

12 $x^2 + 6x + 1 = k(x^2 + 1) = kx^2 + k$

$\Rightarrow x^2(1 - k) + 6x + 1 - k = 0$. **1**

For equal roots the discriminant $= 0$.

This gives $36 - 4(1 - k)(1 - k) = 0$ **1**

$$\Rightarrow (1 - k)^2 = 9$$

$$\Rightarrow 1 - k = \pm 3$$

$$\Rightarrow k = 4 \text{ or } k = -2$$ **2**

Put the quadratic in the form $ax^2 + bx + c = 0$ in order to be able to produce an equation involving the discriminant.

Take care to include the *negative* value of $1 - k$.

Answer	Mark	Examiner's tip

13 (a) $f(x) = 4x^3 - 16x^2 - 19x - 5$

$f(5) = 4 \times 5^3 - 16 \times 5^2 - 19 \times 5 - 5 = 0$

Since $f(5) = 0$, $(x - 5)$ is a factor of $f(x)$
by the factor theorem. **1**

$f(-\tfrac{1}{2}) = 4 \times (-\tfrac{1}{2})^3 - 16 \times (-\tfrac{1}{2})^2$
$\qquad\quad - 19 \times (-\tfrac{1}{2}) - 5 = 0$

By the factor theorem $(x + \tfrac{1}{2})$ is a factor
of $f(x)$ and so $2(x + \tfrac{1}{2})$ is a factor of $f(x)$
i.e. $(2x + 1)$ is a factor of $f(x)$. **1**

Show sufficient working to justify
the statement $f(5) = 0$.

(b) $f(x) = (x - 5)(2x + 1)g(x)$ where $g(x)$
$\hspace{9.5cm}$ is linear

$\quad = (2x^2 - 9x - 5)g(x)$

By inspection, $g(x) = 2x + 1$ **1**

hence $\underline{f(x) = (x - 5)(2x + 1)^2}$ **1**

Check that
$(2x^2 - 9x - 5)(2x + 1)$
$\quad = 4x^3 - 16x^2 - 19x - 5.$

(c)(i) The equation $4e^{3t} - 16e^{2t} - 19e^t - 5 = 0$
is of the form $f(x) = 0$ where $x = e^t$.

From (b) $e^t - 5 = 0$ i.e. $e^t = 5$
or $2e^t + 1 = 0$ (for which there are no
solutions since $e^t > 0$) **1**

Hence <u>there is only one real value of t
satisfying the equation.</u> **1**

(ii) $t = \ln 5 = \underline{1.609}$ (correct to 4 s.f.) **1**

Make sure that you fully justify the
required conclusion.

14 $x + y = 2$ $\hspace{4cm}$ (1)

$x^2 + 2y^2 = 11$ $\hspace{3.5cm}$ (2)

from (1), $x = 2 - y$ **1**

$\Rightarrow x^2 = 4 - 4y + y^2$ $\hspace{2cm}$ (3) **1**

Substituting for x^2 in (2) gives

$\quad 4 - 4y + y^2 + 2y^2 = 11$ **1**

$\Rightarrow 3y^2 - 4y - 7 = 0$

$\Rightarrow (3y - 7)(y + 1) = 0$ **1**

$\Rightarrow y = \tfrac{7}{3}$ or $y = -1$.

When $\underline{y = \tfrac{7}{3}, x = -\tfrac{1}{3}}$ **1**

and when $\underline{y = -1, x = 3}$. **1**

Substitute from the linear equation
into the quadratic.

The idea is to produce a quadratic
in one unknown.

When stating the solution, the
corresponding values of x and y
should be given in pairs.

15 (a) The points of intersection are given by
the simultaneous solution of

$\qquad y = x$ $\hspace{3.5cm}$ (1)

and $\quad x^2 + y^2 - 6x - 2y - 24 = 0.$ $\hspace{0.3cm}$ (2)

Substituting for y in (2) gives

$\quad x^2 + x^2 - 6x - 2x - 24 = 0$ **1**

$\Rightarrow 2x^2 - 8x - 24 = 0$

$\Rightarrow x^2 - 4x - 12 = 0$

$\Rightarrow (x + 2)(x - 6) = 0$

$\Rightarrow x = -2$ or $x = 6$ **1**

There is a common factor of 2 in
each term that can be cancelled to
simplify the equation.

Answer	Mark	Examiner's tip

The coordinates of the points of intersection are

A(6, 6) and B(–2, –2). **1**

Give the answer in the form specified in the question. It is clear from the given diagram which point is A and which is B.

(b) The centre of the circle, with AB as diameter, has coordinates (2, 2).

$$A \nearrow (6,6)$$
$$4$$
$$\overset{4}{\longleftarrow}$$
$$(2,2)$$
$$B \nearrow (-2,-2)$$

It is useful to draw a diagram in order to find the centre and radius of the new circle. Note, the $(\text{radius})^2$ is given by Pythagoras.

Equation of circle is

$(x - 2)^2 + (y - 2)^2 = 32$ **3**

16 (a) $y = 2\log_a 12 - \log_a 9$

$y = \log_a 12^2 - \log_a 9$ **1**

$y = \log_a 144 - \log_a 9$

$y = \log_a \dfrac{144}{9}$

$y = \log_a 16$ **1**

Use the log laws to put the expression for y in the required form.

i.e. The required value of n is 16.

(b) When $a = 2$, $y = \log_2 16$

i.e. $2^y = 16$

$\therefore y = 4$ **1**

The instruction to 'write down' the value of y indicates that no justification is required but this doesn't prevent you from including any workings that you find helpful.

17

(a) Let

$$\frac{1 - x - x^2}{(1 - 2x)(1 - x)^2} \equiv \frac{A}{(1 - 2x)} + \frac{B}{(1 - x)^2} + \frac{C}{(1 - x)}$$

then

$1 - x - x^2 \equiv A(1 - x)^2 + B(1 - 2x) + C(1 - x)(1 - 2x)$

Setting $x = 1$ gives $-1 = -B \Rightarrow B = 1$ **1**

$x = \frac{1}{2}$ gives $\frac{1}{4} = \frac{1}{4} A \Rightarrow A = 1$ **1**

$x = 0$ gives $1 = A + B + C \Rightarrow C = -1$.   **1**

This relationship holds for all values of x.

Select x values that will produce the simplest equations in A, B and C.

Hence,

$$\frac{1 - x - x^2}{(1 - 2x)(1 - x)^2} \equiv \frac{1}{(1 - 2x)} + \frac{1}{(1 - x)^2} - \frac{1}{(1 - x)}$$ **1**

Complete this part of the question by substituting for A, B and C.

(b) $\dfrac{1}{(1 - 2x)} = 1 + 2x + 4x^2 + 8x^3 + ...$ **1**

provided $|2x| < 1$

i.e. $|x| < \frac{1}{2}$

These results are based on the binomial expansion of $(1 - x)^{-1}$ which is an important standard result.

Answer	Mark	Examiner's tip

$$\frac{1}{(1-x)} = 1 + x + x^2 + x^3 + \dots$$

provided $|x| < 1$ — 1

$$\frac{1}{(1-x)^2} = 1 + 2x + 3x^2 + 4x^3 + \dots$$

provided $|x| < 1$ — 1

Hence

$$\frac{1-x-x^2}{(1-2x)(1-x)^2} = 1 + 3x + 6x^2 + 11x^3 + \dots$$ — 2

Note: $\dfrac{1}{(1-x)^2}$ is the derivative of $\dfrac{1}{(1-x)}$ and the corresponding series expansion can be found by differentiating $1 + x + x^2 + x^3 + \dots$ term by term.

(c) The expansion is valid provided $|x| < \frac{1}{2}$. — 1

18 (a) (i) $f(x) = 2x^3 - x^2 - 7x + 6$ — 1
$\Rightarrow f(1) = 2 - 1 - 7 + 6 = 0$
$2x^3 - x^2 - 7x + 6 = (x-1)(2x^2 + x - 6)$ — 1
$\quad = (x-1)(2x-3)(x+2)$ — 2

The hint is that you should now use the factor theorem to identify $(x-1)$ as a factor of $f(x)$.

(ii)

From the graph, $f(x) > 0$ when $-2 < x < 1$ and when $x > \frac{3}{2}$. — 3

A sketch graph is helpful here. Note, the graph has the general shape of a cubic and crosses the x-axis when $x = 1, \frac{3}{2}, -2$ corresponding to the factors found in part (i).

(b) $\dfrac{x^2 + 2x + 7}{(2x+3)(x^2+4)} \equiv \dfrac{A}{(2x+3)} + \dfrac{Bx+C}{(x^2+4)}$

$\Rightarrow x^2 + 2x + 7 \equiv A(x^2+4) + (Bx+C)(2x+3)$

Setting up equations and solving in the usual way gives $A = 1$, $B = 0$ and $C = 1$. — 3

Note: equations in A, B and C can be obtained either by substituting values for x or by comparing like terms. The aim, as always, is to produce the simplest equations to work with.

Hence

$$\int \frac{x^2 + 2x + 7}{(2x+3)(x^2+4)}\,dx = \int \frac{1}{(2x+3)} + \frac{1}{(x^2+4)}\,dx$$

$$= \tfrac{1}{2}\ln|2x+3| + \tfrac{1}{2}\arctan\frac{x}{2} + c$$ — 3

See the chapter on **integration** for advice on the techniques needed here.

Answer	Mark	Examiner's tip

19 (a)

$$f(x) \equiv \frac{x^2 + 6x + 7}{(x+2)(x+3)} \equiv \frac{(x^2 + 5x + 6) + (x+1)}{x^2 + 5x + 6}$$ 1

$$\equiv 1 + \frac{x+1}{(x+2)(x+3)} \equiv A + \frac{B}{(x+2)} + \frac{C}{(x+3)}$$

where $A = 1$, $B = -1$, $C = 2$ 3

(b) $$\int_0^2 f(x)\,dx = \int_0^2 1 - \frac{1}{(x+2)} + \frac{2}{(x+3)}\,dx$$

$$= \left[x - \ln|x+2| + 2\ln|x+3| \right]_0^2$$ 2

$$= 2 - \ln 4 + 2\ln 5 - (0 - \ln 2 + 2\ln 3)$$ 2

$$= 2 + \ln\left(\frac{5^2 \times 2}{4 \times 3^2}\right) = 2 + \ln\left(\frac{25}{18}\right)$$ 3

Examiner's tip: In this case, the numerator and denominator are both of degree 2 and so it is necessary to divide before attempting to use partial fractions.

Since the denominators are linear, the values of B and C can be found quickly using the **cover-up method**.

Note the need to use the log laws to present the final answer in the required form.

2 SEQUENCES AND SERIES

Answer	Mark	Examiner's tip

1 (i) The general term is given by
$$u_k = a + (k-1)d$$
$$\Rightarrow 36 = a + 9d \qquad (1)$$

The sum of the first n terms is given by

$$S_n = \frac{n}{2}(a + l)$$

$$\Rightarrow 180 = \frac{10}{2}(a + a + 9d)$$ 2

$$\Rightarrow 36 = 2a + 9d \qquad (2)$$

From (1) and (2) $a = 0$ and $d = 4$ 2

i.e. the first term is 0 and the common difference is 4.

(ii) $$\sum_{r=1}^{1000}(3r - 1) = 2 + 5 + 8 + \ldots + 2999$$ 2

This is an A.P. with $a = 2$, $d = 3$, $n = 1000$ and $l = 2999$.

$$S_{1000} = \frac{1000}{2}(2 + 2999)$$

$$= 1\ 500\ 500$$ 1

Examiner's tip: It's a good idea to label equations that will be needed later.

Solve equations (1) and (2) simultaneously.

Substitute $r = 1, 2, 3$ and 1000 to get an idea of how the series develops.

The fact that the series is an A.P. is very significant and worth stating.

Answer	**Mark**	**Examiner's tip**

2 (a) $S_\infty = \dfrac{a}{1-r}$ $\qquad S_8 = \dfrac{a(1-r^8)}{1-r}$

Express the given information using the standard notation and formulas to produce an equation.

$S_8 = \tfrac{1}{2}S_\infty \Rightarrow 1 - r^8 = \tfrac{1}{2} \Rightarrow r^8 = \tfrac{1}{2}$

$\qquad\qquad \Rightarrow \underline{r = 0.917}$ (correct to 3 d.p.) **3**

17 th term $= ar^{16} = 10$

Note: $r^{16} = (r^8)^2 = \left(\tfrac{1}{2}\right)^2 = \tfrac{1}{4}$.

$\Rightarrow a = \dfrac{10}{(0.917...)^{16}} \Rightarrow a = 40$ **2**

It follows that the *exact* value of a is 40. If the value of a is found by calculator, then take care to work with the full available accuracy of the result for r and not the *rounded* value (0.917), given above.

(b) Using $S_n = \dfrac{n}{2}(2a + (n-1)d)$

$10\,000 = \dfrac{n}{2}(2a + 10(n-1)) = n(a + 5(n-1))$

$\Rightarrow a = \dfrac{10\,000}{n} - 5(n-1)$ **2**

n th term is $a + (n-1)d$

$= \dfrac{10\,000}{n} - 5(n-1) + 10(n-1)$

$= \dfrac{10\,000}{n} + 5(n-1)$ **1**

$\Rightarrow \dfrac{10\,000}{n} + 5(n-1) < 500$

Note: n can only take positive whole number values but the graph of the associated equation

$y = x^2 - 101x + 2000$

in continuous variables x and y, can reveal important information about the behaviour of

$n^2 - 101n + 2000.$

$\Rightarrow 10\,000 + 5n^2 - 5n < 500n \quad$ (since $n > 0$)

$\Rightarrow 5n^2 - 505n + 10\,000 < 0$

$\Rightarrow n^2 - 101n + 2000 < 0$

The larger root of the equation
$x^2 - 101x + 2000 = 0$

is given by $x = \dfrac{101 + \sqrt{101^2 - 8000}}{2}$

$= 73.957...$

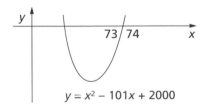

Hence, the largest possible value of n is $\underline{73}$. **4**

3 (a) When ball strikes floor for third time, total

distance travelled is $1 + 2\left(\tfrac{3}{5}\right) + 2\left(\tfrac{3}{5}\right)^2 = \underline{2.92\text{ m}}$ **3**

(b) Total distance travelled cannot exceed

$1 + 2\left(\tfrac{3}{5}\right) + 2\left(\tfrac{3}{5}\right)^2 + 2\left(\tfrac{3}{5}\right)^3 + \ldots = \dfrac{2}{\left(1 - \tfrac{3}{5}\right)} - 1$

It is necessary to subtract 1 from the sum of the infinite G.P. because the first term is 1 (*not* 2).

$= \underline{4\text{ m}}.$ **4**

Answer	Mark	Examiner's tip

4 (a) The first four terms of $(1 + kx)^8$ are given by

$$1 + 8kx + \frac{8 \times 7}{2!}(kx)^2 + \frac{8 \times 7 \times 6}{3!}(kx)^3$$

$$= 1 + 8kx + 28k^2x^2 + 56k^3x^3 \qquad \text{4}$$

Comparing with the given result gives

$8k = 12 \Rightarrow \underline{k = 1.5}, \quad p = 28k^2 \Rightarrow \underline{p = 63}$ **3**

and $q = 56k^3 \Rightarrow \underline{q = 189}$

(b) Coefficient of x^3 is given by $q - p = \underline{126}$ **4**

It's a good idea to write the expansion in full first and then simplify it. This is particularly important where minus signs are involved.

The two expansions are equivalent and so corresponding coefficients must be equal.

---

5 $(1 + x)^5 = 1 + 5x + 10x^2 + 10x^3 + 5x^4 + x^5$ **1**

Letting $x = z + z^2$, the only terms containing z^3 are:

$10x^2 = 10(z + z^2)^2 = 10(z^2 + 2z^3 + z^4)$

and $10x^3 = 10(z + z^2)^3$

$\qquad = 10(z^3 + \dots \text{terms in higher powers})$

The sum of the terms in z^3 is given by

$20z^3 + 10z^3 = 30z^3$.

Hence, the required coefficient of z^3 is 30.   **4**

In this case, the simplest way to obtain the coefficients of the powers of x is to use Pascal's Triangle.

$$
\begin{array}{ccccccccccc}
 & & & & & 1 & & & & & \\
 & & & & 1 & & 1 & & & & \\
 & & & 1 & & 2 & & 1 & & & \\
 & & 1 & & 3 & & 3 & & 1 & & \\
 & 1 & & 4 & & 6 & & 4 & & 1 & \\
1 & & 5 & & 10 & & 10 & & 5 & & 1
\end{array}
$$

Note: There is no need to work out the complete expansion of $(1 + z + z^2)^5$. It is only necessary to consider the terms in which z^3 will appear.

---

6 (i) $(1 - 2x)^{\frac{1}{2}} = 1 + \frac{1}{2}(-2x) + \frac{\frac{1}{2}(-\frac{1}{2})}{2!}(-2x)^2$

$+ \frac{\frac{1}{2}(-\frac{1}{2})(-\frac{3}{2})}{3!}(-2x)^3 + \frac{\frac{1}{2}(-\frac{1}{2})(-\frac{3}{2})(-\frac{5}{2})}{4!}(-2x)^4 + \dots$

$= 1 - x - \frac{x^2}{2} - \frac{x^3}{2} - \frac{5x^4}{8} - \dots$

valid for $|2x| < 1$

     i.e. $|x| < \frac{1}{2}$.   **6**

> *Note: The binomial expansion of $(2 + x)^{\frac{1}{2}}$ for example, could be worked out as $2^{\frac{1}{2}}\left(1 + \dfrac{x}{2}\right)^{\frac{1}{2}}$ and would be valid for $\left|\dfrac{x}{2}\right| < 1$ i.e for $|x| < 2$.*

(ii) $\sqrt{0.8} = (1 - 2 \times 0.1)^{\frac{1}{2}}$

$\approx 1 - 0.1 - \frac{0.1^2}{2} - \frac{0.1^3}{2} - \frac{5 \times 0.1^4}{8}$

$= 0.894\ 437\ 5$

$\Rightarrow \underline{\sqrt{0.8} = 0.8944}$ (correct to four d.p.)   **4**

Note: The series expansion established in part (i) is valid when $x = 0.1$ and so the required result may be obtained by substitution.

This result is easily checked by using the square root function directly.

Answer	Mark	Examiner's tip

7 $(1-4x)^{-\frac{1}{2}} = 1 + (-\frac{1}{2})(-4x) + \dfrac{(-\frac{1}{2})(-\frac{3}{2})}{2}(-4x)^2$

$\qquad + \dfrac{(-\frac{1}{2})(-\frac{3}{2})(-\frac{5}{2})}{3!}(-4x)^3 + \dots$

$\qquad = 1 + 2x + 6x^2 + 20x^3 + \dots$ **4**

Use brackets and include all minus signs before attempting to simplify the result. It is important, here, to appreciate the structure of the question so that the link between the parts is recognised. Questions often follow a pattern in which the results established early on may be **used** later.

$\dfrac{(1-3x)}{\sqrt{1-4x}} = (1-3x)(1-4x)^{-\frac{1}{2}}$

$\qquad = (1-3x)(1 + 2x + 6x^2 + 20x^3 + \dots)$

Considering only the terms in x^3 we have

$20x^3 - 18x^3 = 2x^3$

and so the coefficient of x^3 is 2. **2**

Be **clear** about what the question requires you to do. In this case there is no need to work out the full expansion.

8 (a) $t_n = 1 - \dfrac{1}{n}$

as $n \to \infty, \dfrac{1}{n} \to 0.$

$\Rightarrow$ as $n \to \infty, t_n \to 1$

In this case, the behaviour of the sequence as n increases is clear, and so the most convincing approach is to deduce the result as shown.

It follows that t_n defines a <u>convergent</u> sequence. **1**

(b) $u_n = 1 - \dfrac{1}{u_{n-1}},$ where $u_1 = 2$

Using the definition,

$u_2 = 1 - \tfrac{1}{2} = \tfrac{1}{2}, u_3 = 1 - \dfrac{1}{\left(\frac{1}{2}\right)} = 1 - 2 = -1$

It is not immediately apparent just how the sequence will develop and so it's a good idea to apply the definition to find the value of some terms.

$u_4 = 1 - \dfrac{1}{(-1)} = 1 - (-1) = 2 = u_1.$

It follows that the sequence will continue as:
$2, \tfrac{1}{2}, -1, 2, \tfrac{1}{2}, -1, \dots$
and so the sequence is <u>periodic</u> (with period 3). **3**

The sequence is *divergent*, because the terms do not approach a limit, **but** the most informative description is that it is *periodic* (with period 3) because after every 3 terms the sequence repeats itself.

Answer	Mark	Examiner's tip

9 (a) (i)
$$(ar)^2 = ar^3$$
$$\Rightarrow \quad a^2r^2 = ar^3$$
$$\Rightarrow \quad a^2r^2 - ar^3 = 0$$
$$\Rightarrow \quad ar^2(a - r) = 0$$
$$\Rightarrow \quad a = r \qquad (1)$$

	Mark	
	2	Re-write the given information as an equation. Make sure you square (ar); do not write ar^2.
	2	

$$\frac{a}{1 - r} = 1 \Rightarrow a = 1 - r \qquad (2)$$

2   Use the results for the sum to infinity of a G.P.

From (1) and (2) $\quad \underline{a = r = \tfrac{1}{2}}$

2   Find simultaneous solutions.

(ii) $S_{10} = \dfrac{\tfrac{1}{2}\left(1 - (\tfrac{1}{2})^{10}\right)}{1 - \tfrac{1}{2}} = 1 - (\tfrac{1}{2})^{10}$

   Substitute the results found in (i) in the formula for the sum of a G.P.

$$= 0.999\,023\,4\ldots$$

3

$$\text{i.e. } \underline{S_{10} > 0.999}$$

1

(b) (i) The nth term is $\log_e y^n$.

1

The sum to n terms is
$$\log_e y + \log_e y^2 + \log_e y^3 + \ldots + \log_e y^n$$

1   Note that the common difference is $\log_e y$.

$$= \log_e y + 2\log_e y + 3\log_e y + \ldots + n\log_e y$$

1

$$= \frac{n}{2}(\log_e y + n\log_e y)$$

2   Use $S_n = \dfrac{n}{2}(a + 1)$

$$= \frac{n(n + 1)}{2}\log_e y$$

1

(ii) The nth term is $\underline{\log_e(xy^n)}$.

1   Always look for opportunities to make use of results established earlier in the question.

$$\log_e(xy) + \log_e(xy^2) + \log_e(xy^3) + \ldots + \log_e(xy^n)$$

1

$$= (\log_e x + \log_e y) + (\log_e x + \log_e y^2) + \ldots + (\log_e x + \log_e y^n)$$

1

$$= n\log_e x + (\log_e y + \log_e y^2 + \ldots + \log_e y^n)$$

2   Use the results from b(i).

$$= n\log_e x + \frac{n(n + 1)}{2}\log_e y$$

2

10 (a) The value in 1993 is given by u_3 in each model.

The $\boxed{\text{Ans}}$ key on your calculator provides a simple method of generating sequences.

Model 1	$u_1 = £4500$		
	$u_2 = £4000$		
	$\underline{u_3 = £3500}$	1	Use $\boxed{\text{Ans}} - 500$

Model 2	$u_1 = £4500$		
	$u_2 = £4050$		
	$\underline{u_3 = £3645}$	1	Use $0.9 \boxed{\text{Ans}}$

Model 3	$u_1 = £4400$		
	$u_2 = £3920$		
	$\underline{u_3 = £3536}$	2	Use $0.8 \boxed{\text{Ans}} + 400$

Answer	Mark	Examiner's tip
(b) Model 1 gives u_8 = £1000 Model 2 gives u_8 = £2152.34 Model 3 gives u_8 = £2503.32	1	This mark is for correctly applying each model.
The owner is using Model 2.	1	This mark is for the correct conclusion.
(c) (i) $V = 0.8V + 400$	1	The limiting value has the property that it is unchanged by the process given in the model. This gives
(ii) $0.2V = 400$		
$\therefore V = 2000$	1	$u_{n+1} = u_n = V$. Substitute this information into the model to give the required equation.

11 (a) $\quad f(r) - f(r+1) = \dfrac{1}{r(r+1)} - \dfrac{1}{(r+1)(r+2)}$ — 1

Use the definition to obtain an expression for $f(r) - f(r+1)$.

$$= \dfrac{(r+2) - r}{r(r+1)(r+2)}$$

Use a common denominator to subtract the fractions and simplify to verify the result.

hence $f(r) - f(r+1) = \dfrac{2}{r(r+1)(r+2)}$ — 1

(b) Let S_n denote the sum to n terms of the given series.

Introducing S_n makes it easier to show the method clearly.

Then $2S_n = \dfrac{2}{1.2.3} + \dfrac{2}{2.3.4} + \dots$

Working with $2S_n$ initially simplifies the algebra.

$$\dots + \dfrac{2}{n(n+1)(n+2)}$$

$$= (f(1) - f(2)) + (f(2) - f(3)) + \dots$$
$$\dots + (f(n) - f(n+1))$$

Note how all but the first and last terms cancel.

i.e. $2S_n = f(1) - f(n+1)$ — 1

$$= \dfrac{1}{2} - \dfrac{1}{(n+1)(n+2)}$$

$$= \dfrac{(n+1)(n+2) - 2}{2(n+1)(n+2)}$$

$$= \dfrac{n^2 + 3n}{2(n+1)(n+2)} = \dfrac{n(n+3)}{2(n+1)(n+2)}$$ — 1

So $S_n = \dfrac{n(n+3)}{4(n+1)(n+2)}$ — 1

Divide both sides by 2 at the end.

3 COORDINATE GEOMETRY

Answer	Mark	Examiner's tip

1

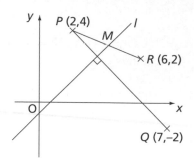

$$\text{Gradient of } PQ = \frac{4-(-2)}{2-7} = -\frac{6}{5}$$

$\therefore$ Gradient of $l = \frac{5}{6}$

Coordinates of M are $(4, 3)$.

Equation of l :

using $y - y_1 = m(x - x_1)$

$$y - 3 = \frac{5}{6}(x - 4)$$

$$6y - 18 = 5x - 20$$

$$\underline{6y - 5x + 2 = 0}$$

Marks (right column):

1

2

1

1

Examiner's tips (right column):

Draw a sketch, of reasonable size, to show all the information. It is then much easier to see what is required.

Remember that $m_1 \times m_2 = -1$ when lines are perpendicular. This is an important result and often features in coordinate geometry questions.

The sketch is useful in checking the mid-point.

It does not matter in which format you give your answer. It could be

$$6y = 5x - 2$$

or $y = \frac{5}{6}x - \frac{1}{3}$

2

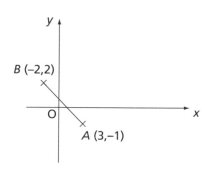

$$\text{Gradient of } AB = \frac{2-(-1)}{-2-3} = -\frac{3}{5}$$

Equation of AB :

using $y - y_1 = m(x - x_1)$

$$y - 2 = -\frac{3}{5}(x - (-2))$$

$$5y - 10 = -3x - 6$$

$$\underline{3x + 5y - 4 = 0}$$

At point of intersection with the x-axis, $y = 0$

$$\Rightarrow 3x - 4 = 0, \ x = \frac{4}{3}$$

$$\underline{\text{Coordinates are } \left(\frac{4}{3}, 0\right)}$$

Marks (right column):

1

1

1

1

1

Examiner's tips (right column):

To find the equation, you could use the formula

$$\frac{y - y_1}{x - x_1} = \frac{y_2 - y_1}{x_2 - x_1}$$

but you need to be careful with the coordinates and signs.

The diagram provides a check for the sign of the gradient.

State the final answer, otherwise you may lose the mark.

Answer	Mark	Examiner's tip

3 $3x + 4y - 36 = 0$

At B, $y = 0 \Rightarrow 3x = 36$, $x = 12$ so B is $(12, 0)$

At C, $x = 0 \Rightarrow 4y = 36$, $y = 9$ so C is $(0, 9)$

(a)

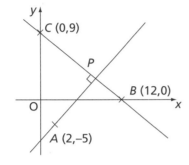

Put all the information obtained so far onto a diagram.

From the diagram:

Gradient of $BC = -\frac{3}{4}$

$\Rightarrow$ Gradient of $AP = \frac{4}{3}$ **1**

The diagram has been useful for obtaining the gradient of BC directly.

Equation of AP:

$$y - y_1 = m(x - x_1)$$
$$y - (-5) = \frac{4}{3}(x - 2)$$
$$3y + 15 = 4x - 8$$
$$\Rightarrow \underline{4x - 3y - 23 = 0}$$ **1**

(b) To find the coordinates of P:

P lies on $AP \Rightarrow 4x - 3y - 23 = 0$	(1)	
P lies on $BC \Rightarrow 3x + 4y - 36 = 0$	(2)	
(1) $\times$ 4 $16x - 12y - 92 = 0$	(3)	
(2) $\times$ 3 $9x + 12y - 108 = 0$	(4)	
(3) + 4 $25x \qquad - 200 = 0$		
$x = 8$		

Label each equation for easy reference and explain your working.

Substitute in (2) $24 + 4y - 36 = 0$

$$y = 3$$

$\therefore$ $\underline{P \text{ has coordinates } (8, 3)}$ **2**

By Pythagoras' Theorem

$$AP^2 = (8 - 2)^2 + (3 - (-5))^2$$
$$= 100$$
$$\Rightarrow AP = 10$$

<u>The perpendicular distance from</u>   **1**

<u>A to BC is 10 units</u>

It is quicker if you recognise the Pythagorean triple 6, 8, 10. Be on the look out for them.

Answer	Mark	Examiner's tip

(c) Area $\triangle ABC = \frac{1}{2} \times CB \times AP$

CB can be found from $\triangle OCB$

$CB^2 = 9^2 + 12^2 = 225 \Rightarrow CB = 15$ **1**

Area $\triangle ABC = \frac{1}{2} \times 15 \times 10$

$= 75$ square units   **1**

To find CB you need to focus your attention on a different triangle, $\triangle OCB$.

Another Pythagorean triple has been used!

4 $l : 2x - y - 1 = 0 \Rightarrow y = 2x - 1$

so gradient $= 2$, y-intercept $= -1$ **1**

(a) m: gradient $= -\frac{1}{2}$, y-intercept $= 4$

so equation of m is $\underline{y = -\frac{1}{2}x + 4}$ **2**

The format '$y = mx + c$' is useful here, but be careful with notation, since m has been used for the name of the line.

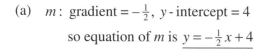
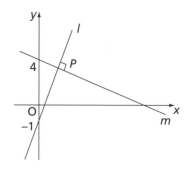

At P, $y = 2x - 1$ and $y = -\frac{1}{2}x + 4$

$\therefore 2x - 1 = -\frac{1}{2}x + 4$

$\frac{5}{2}x = 5$

$x = 2$

When $x = 2$, $y = 2(2) - 1 = 3$

$\therefore \underline{P \text{ is } (2, 3)}$ as required   **1**

The substitution method is a good one to use to solve the simultaneous equations.

(b)

It is helpful to draw another diagram so that you are clear about where the lines and points are.

Answer	Mark	Examiner's tip

Equation of n:

$y - y_1 = m(x - x_1)$

$y - 0 = -\frac{1}{2}(x - 3)$

$\underline{2y = -x + 3}$ 2

At Q, $2y = -x + 3$ and $y = 2x - 1$ 1

$\therefore 2(2x - 1) = -x + 3$

$5x = 5$

$x = 1, \ y = 2(1) - 1 = 1$

$\therefore \underline{Q \text{ has coordinates } (1,1)}$ 1

(c) $AP^2 = 2^2 + 1^2 = 5 \Rightarrow AP = \sqrt{5}$ Leave the lengths in surd form.

$BQ^2 = 2^2 + 1^2 = 5 \Rightarrow BQ = \sqrt{5}$

$PQ^2 = 1^2 + 2^2 = 5 \Rightarrow PQ = \sqrt{5}$ 3

$\therefore \underline{AP = BQ = PQ}$ 1   State the final result, do not leave it to be assumed.

5 (i) $AB = \sqrt{50}, \ BC = \sqrt{98}, \ AC = \sqrt{148}$ You will need to draw your own

from which the result follows.   4   diagram showing the coordinates.

(Check for your values   The lengths can be found using

that $AB^2 + BC^2 = CA^2$) $d^2 = (x_2 - x_1)^2 + (y_2 - y_1)^2.$

$A\hat{B}C = 90°$ 1   Leave them in surd form.

(ii)   Gradient $AB = 1$, gradient $BC = -1$

Since products of gradients $= -1$,

$A\hat{B}C = 90°$ 3

(iii) $MA = MB = \sqrt{37}$ 3   Use the mid-point formula

$\left(\frac{1}{2}(x_1 + x_2), \frac{1}{2}(y_1 + y_2)\right)$

to find M (6, 1) and work out MA and MB.

(iv) $(x - 6)^2 + (y - 1)^2 = 37$ 3   Note the instruction to 'write down' which infers that the result is clear from what has already been established.
Remember that the angle in a semicircle is 90°, so AC is a diameter, M the centre.

Answer	Mark	Examiner's tip

6 (a) Gradient of $AB = \dfrac{6-0}{5-1} = \dfrac{3}{2}$ — **1**

Equation of AB: $\dfrac{y-0}{x-1} = \dfrac{3}{2}$

$$\underline{2y = 3x - 3}$$ — **2**

(b)
$$2x + 3y = 15 \quad (1)$$
$$3x - 2y = 3 \quad (2)$$

(1) × 2 $\quad 4x + 6y = 30 \quad (3)$
(2) × 3 $\quad \underline{9x - 6y = 9} \quad (4)$

Add $\quad 13x \quad = 39$
$\quad x = 3$ — **2**

Substitute in (1) $\quad 6 + 3y = 15$
$\quad y = 3$ — **1**

∴ C has coordinates $\underline{(3, 3)}$

(c) When $x = -3,$ $\quad -6 + 3y = 15$
$\quad 3y = 21$
$\quad y = 7$

P is the point $(-3, 7)$ — **1**

$PA^2 = (1 - (-3))^2 + (0 - 7)^2$
$\quad = 65$ — **1** — There is no need to find PA or PB here since it is sufficient to show that $PA^2 = PB^2$.

$PB^2 = (5 - (-3))^2 + (6 - 7)^2$
$\quad = 65$ — **1**

Since $PA^2 = PB^2$, $\underline{PA = PB}$ — **1**

4 FUNCTIONS

Answer	Mark	Examiner's tip

1 $f : x \to \dfrac{1}{2-x} + 3 \quad x \in \mathbb{R}, \ x \neq 2$

(a) $f(5) = \dfrac{1}{2-5} + 3 = -\tfrac{1}{3} + 3 = 2\tfrac{2}{3}.$

$ff(5) = f(2\tfrac{2}{3}) = \dfrac{1}{2 - 2\tfrac{2}{3}} + 3 = -\tfrac{3}{2} + 3 = 1\tfrac{1}{2}.$ ⟶ 1

$ff(k)$ is not defined when $\underline{k = 3}$ ⟶ 1

$f(3) = 2$ and so $ff(3) = f(2)$ which is not defined since 2 is not in the domain of f.

(b) Let $\dfrac{1}{2-x} + 3 = y$

then $\dfrac{1}{2-x} = y - 3 \ \Rightarrow 2 - x = \dfrac{1}{y-3}$

Making x the subject of this equation allows us to identify the reverse process needed for the inverse function.

$\Rightarrow x = 2 - \dfrac{1}{y-3}$ ⟶ 1

The reverse process is now defined in terms of the variable x.

It follows that $\underline{f^{-1}(x) = 2 - \dfrac{1}{x-3}}.$ ⟶ 1

The domain of f^{-1} is given by $x \in \mathbb{R}, \ x \neq 3.$ ⟶ 1

2 (a) $k(x) = f(g(x)) = f(3 - 2x) = 2(3 - 2x) - 1$ ⟶ 1

$\therefore \underline{k(x) = 5 - 4x}$ ⟶ 1

(b) $h(k(x)) = h(5 - 4x) = \tfrac{1}{4}\big(5 - (5 - 4x)\big)$ ⟶ 1

Care is needed here with the use of brackets.

$= \tfrac{1}{4} \times 4x$

$\therefore \underline{h(k(x)) = x}$ ⟶ 1

(c) $\underline{h = k^{-1}}$ ⟶ 1

Note: The wording of part (c) provides a clue to the expected result.

3 (a) $g : x \to x^2 + 1, \quad x \in \mathbb{R}$

The minimum value of $g(x)$ is 1, since $x^2 \geq 0.$

So, the range of g is given by $\underline{\{x : x \geq 1\}}$ ⟶ 1

(b) $gf(x) = fg(x) \Rightarrow g(3x - 1) = f(x^2 + 1)$

Care is needed to avoid algebraic errors, particularly in the use of brackets.

$\Rightarrow (3x - 1)^2 + 1 = 3(x^2 + 1) - 1$ ⟶ 2

$\Rightarrow 9x^2 - 6x + 2 = 3x^2 + 2$

$\Rightarrow 6x^2 - 6x = 0$ ⟶ 2

Don't be tempted to divide throughout by x, or the solution $x = 0$ may be lost.

$\Rightarrow 6x(x - 1) = 0$

$\Rightarrow \underline{x = 0 \ \text{or} \ x = 1}.$ ⟶ 1

Answer	Mark	Examiner's tip

(c) $|f(x)| = 8 \Rightarrow f(x) = 8$ or $f(x) = -8$. — **1**

$f(x) = 8 \Rightarrow 3x - 1 = 8 \Rightarrow x = 3$

$f(x) = -8 \Rightarrow 3x - 1 = -8 \Rightarrow x = -2\frac{1}{3}$

hence, the required values are 3 and $-2\frac{1}{3}$ — **2**

Note how the solution branches to take the effect of the modulus function into account.

(d) $h(x) = x^2 + 3x = \left(x + \frac{3}{2}\right)^2 - \frac{9}{4}$

hence, the least value of q is $-\frac{3}{2}$. — **2**

The required value of q corresponds to the turning point on the graph, since for smaller values h will be many-one.

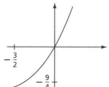

2

4 (i)   (ii)

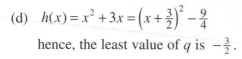
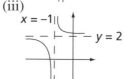

3

*Both branches of the curve **must** be shown for full credit.*

(iii)

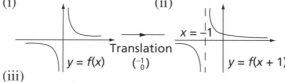

2

Label the asymptotes so that the effect of the transformations is made clear.

$$f(x+1) + 2 = \frac{1}{x+1} + 2 = \frac{1 + 2(x+1)}{x+1}$$

$$= \frac{2x+3}{x+1}$$ — **2**

The hint, provided by the structure of the question, is that $f(x+1) + 2$ should be expanded and compared with $\dfrac{2x+3}{x+1}$.

The graph of $y = \dfrac{2x+3}{x+1}$ is the same as the graph of $y = f(x+1) + 2$ and so is symmetrical about $(-1, 2)$. — **1**

5 (a) The range of f is $\{x : x \geq -1\}$

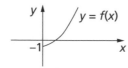

1

Note: $\{y : y \geq -1\}$ and $\{x : x \geq -1\}$ describe the same set *of numbers. By convention, x is usually used.*

(b) Since the domain of f is restricted to non-negative values f is one-one and so has an inverse function. — **1**

Note: The graph must not extend to the left of the y-axis since the corresponding x values are not in the domain.

Let $4x^2 - 1 = y$ then $x = \frac{1}{2}\sqrt{y+1}$

so $f^{-1}(x) = \frac{1}{2}\sqrt{x+1}$ — **2**

Answer	Mark	Examiner's tip

(c) $fg(x) = f\left(\sqrt{(x+6)}\right) = 4(x+6) - 1 = 4x + 23$

$fg(x) \geq f(x) \Rightarrow 4x + 23 \geq 4x^2 - 1$

$\Rightarrow x^2 - x - 6 \leq 0$

$\Rightarrow (x+2)(x-3) \leq 0$ **1**

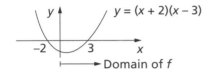

1

From the sketch, $fg(x) \geq f(x) \Rightarrow \underline{0 \leq x \leq 3}$ **1**

An alternative approach is to add the graph of $y = 4x + 23$ to the graph given in part (a). The intersection of the graphs is found by solving $4x + 23 = 4x^2 - 1$ and the solution of $fg(x) \geq f(x)$ is, again, seen to be $0 \leq x \leq 3$.

Care is needed to ensure that only those values of x in the domain are included in the solution.

5 TRIGONOMETRY

Answer	Mark	Examiner's tip

1

Arc length $= r\theta$ (θ in radians)

$r\theta = \frac{1}{2}P \Rightarrow 2r = \frac{1}{2}P$

$\therefore \quad r\theta = 2r$

$\theta = 2$ **2**

Area $= \frac{1}{2}r^2\theta$

$= \underline{r^2}$ **1**

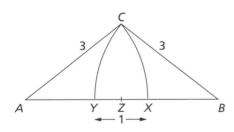

This question contains no structure, so you have to decide where to start. A good diagram with the information inserted will help you to spot that $2r = r\theta$.

You could do $s = r\theta$, $P = 2r + r\theta$

$\Rightarrow r\theta = \frac{1}{2}(2r + r\theta)$

$2r\theta = 2r + r\theta$

$r\theta = 2r$ as before.

Note that the question is far more complicated if you work in degrees.

2

$AZ = \frac{1}{2}AB = 2.5$ cm

$AX = 3$ cm (radius)

$\therefore \; ZX = ZY = 0.5$ cm

and $YX = 1$ cm

Deduce missing lengths from the information given and state them clearly.

Answer	Mark	Examiner's tip

(a)

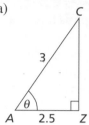

$$\theta = \cos^{-1}\left(\tfrac{2.5}{3}\right)$$
$$= \underline{0.5857 \text{ radians (4 d.p.)}} \quad 1$$

Set your calculator to RAD; give answer to the accuracy stated.

(b) (i) Arc $CX = 3\theta$, $YX = 1$ cm
  so perimeter of $R = 6\theta + 1$
  $= \underline{4.51 \text{ cm (3 s.f.)}} \quad 1$

Retain the value for θ on your calculator and use the uncorrected value in subsequent working.

(ii) Area sector $ACX = \tfrac{1}{2} \times 3^2 \times \theta$
  $= \underline{2.64 \text{ cm}^2 \text{ (3 s.f.)}} \quad 1$

(iii) Area of $\triangle ACB = \tfrac{1}{2} \times 3 \times 5 \times \sin\theta$
  $= \underline{4.145...\text{cm}^2}$

Area of $CXB = \triangle - $ sector
Area of $R = \triangle - 2(\triangle - \text{sector})$
  $= 2 \times \text{sector area} - \triangle$
  $= 2(2.635...) - 4.145...$
  $= \underline{1.13 \text{ cm}^2 \text{ (2 d.p.)}} \quad 2$

There are several ways of calculating the area of R. Explain your method carefully.

3 Area of sector $OAB = \tfrac{1}{2} \times 10^2 \times \theta$
  $= 50\theta \text{ cm}^2 \quad 1$

Area of $\triangle OAB = \tfrac{1}{2} \times 10^2 \times \sin\theta$
  $= 50\sin\theta \text{ cm}^2 \quad 1$

$\therefore$ Area of minor segment $= \underline{50(\theta - \sin\theta) \text{ cm}^2} \quad 1$

Remember the formula $A = \tfrac{1}{2}r^2\theta$ for the area of a sector, when θ is in *radians*.

Area of a $\triangle = \tfrac{1}{2}ab\sin C$

(i) $50(\theta - \sin\theta) = \tfrac{1}{20} \times \pi \times 100 \quad 1$
  $10\theta - 10\sin\theta = \pi$
  $10\sin\theta = 10\theta - \pi$
  $\sin\theta = \theta - \tfrac{\pi}{10} \quad 1$

Be careful with the algebra here.

(ii) When $\theta = 1.27$

  LHS $= \sin\theta = 0.9551... \quad 1$
  RHS $= \theta - \tfrac{1}{10}\pi$
  $= 1.27 - \tfrac{1}{10}\pi = 0.9558... \quad 1$

  Since LHS $\approx$ RHS
  $\theta = 1.27$ satisfies the equation approximately.

Remember to set your calculator to radians.
Take care how you write out your working for this.
Do not write
$\sin 1.27 = 1.27 - \tfrac{1}{10}\pi$
which leads to
$0.9551... = 0.9558...$

Answer	Mark	Examiner's tip

(iii) π radians $= 180°$

1.27 radians $= \dfrac{180}{\pi} \times 1.27$ 1

$\qquad\qquad = 72.76\ldots$
$\qquad\qquad = 73°$ (correct to 2 s.f.)   1

4 (a) $6\sin^2 x = 5 + \cos x$

$6(1 - \cos^2 x) = 5 + \cos x$ 1

$6 - 6\cos^2 x = 5 + \cos x$

$6\cos^2 x + \cos x - 1 = 0$ 1

$(3\cos x - 1)(2\cos x + 1) = 0$

$\Rightarrow \underline{\cos x = \tfrac{1}{3} \text{ or } \cos x = -\tfrac{1}{2}}$ 2

This is a common type of question. If you change the format of $\sin^2 x$ you can form a quadratic equation in $\cos x$.

(b) $\cos x = \tfrac{1}{3}$,

principal value $= \cos^{-1}\left(\tfrac{1}{3}\right) = 70.52\ldots°$

$\cos x = -\tfrac{1}{2}$,

principal value $= \cos^{-1}\left(-\tfrac{1}{2}\right) = 120°$

In the range $180° < x < 540°$

The calculator does not give answers in the required range.

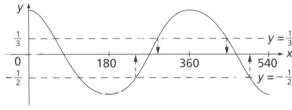

$x = 360 \pm 70.52\ldots$

$\qquad = 289.5°,\ 430.5°$ (1 d.p.)   2

$x = 360 \pm 120 = 240°,\ 480°$ 2

$\therefore\ \underline{x = 240°,\ 289.5°,\ 430.5°,\ 480°}$

You could work out the answers by using the quadrant diagram

$$\begin{array}{c|c} S & A \\ \hline T & C \end{array} \quad \text{and using symmetry.}$$

5 (a)

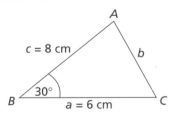

Using the cos rule

$b^2 = a^2 + c^2 - 2ac\cos B$ 1

$\quad = 6^2 + 8^2 - 2(6)(8)\cos 30°$

$\quad = 16.86\ldots$ 1

$\underline{b = 4.11 \text{ cm}}$ (3 s.f.)   1

State the rule and show what values you are substituting.
Make sure your calculator is set to DEG mode.

Answers to Unit 5

Answer	Mark	Examiner's tip

(b) By the sine rule

$$\frac{\sin A}{a} = \frac{\sin B}{b}$$ — 1 — Use the uncorrected value for b found above.

$$\sin A = \frac{6 \sin 30°}{4.106\ldots} = 0.7305\ldots$$ — 1

$$\underline{A = 46.9° \ (1 \text{ d.p.})}$$ — 1

6 $f(A) = \dfrac{\cos A}{1 + \sin A} + \dfrac{1 + \sin A}{\cos A}$

(a) $f(A) = \dfrac{\cos^2 A + (1 + \sin A)^2}{\cos A \ (1 + \sin A)}$ — 1

$$= \frac{\cos^2 A + 1 + 2\sin A + \sin^2 A}{\cos A \ (1 + \sin A)}$$

$$= \frac{2 + 2 \sin A}{\cos A \ (1 + \sin A)}$$ — 1 — Remember that $\cos^2 A + \sin^2 A = 1$.

$$= \frac{2(1 + \sin A)}{\cos A \ (1 + \sin A)}$$

$$= \underline{2 \sec A}$$ — 1

(b) $\quad f(A) = 4$ — Use the format for $f(A)$ obtained in part (a).

$\therefore 2 \sec A = 4$

$\sec A = 2$

$\cos A = 0.5$ — 1 — Don't forget that there are two

$\underline{A = 60°, 300°}$ — 1 — solutions in the required range.

7 $\sin 3\theta = \sin(2\theta + \theta)$ — Knowledge of the use of trig

$= \sin 2\theta \cos \theta + \cos 2\theta \sin \theta$ — identities is needed here. Use your

$= 2 \sin \theta \cos \theta \cos \theta + (1 - 2 \sin^2\theta) \sin \theta$ — formulas booklet to check your

$= 2 \sin \theta \cos^2\theta + \sin \theta - 2\sin^3\theta$ — accuracy, so that you can progress

$= 2 \sin \theta(1 - \sin^2\theta) + \sin \theta - 2\sin^3\theta$ — confidently. Notice that the result

$= 2 \sin \theta - 2 \sin^3\theta + \sin \theta - 2\sin^3\theta$ — contains only terms in $\sin \theta$.

$= \underline{3 \sin \theta - 4 \sin^3\theta}$ — 3

$\sin 3\theta = 2 \sin \theta$ — Refer to first part of question.

$\Rightarrow 3 \sin \theta - 4 \sin^3\theta = 2 \sin \theta$ — There are several traps that you

$\sin \theta - 4 \sin^3\theta = 0$ — might fall into. If you 'cancel' $\sin \theta$,

$\sin \theta(1 - 4 \sin^2\theta) = 0$ — you will lose some solutions. Also

$\sin \theta(1 - 2 \sin \theta)(1 + 2 \sin \theta) = 0$ — 2 — you should factorise the equation

$\therefore \sin \theta = 0$ or $\sin \theta = \pm\frac{1}{2}$ — 1 — fully so that you realise that

$\sin \theta = 0 \Rightarrow \theta = 0, 180°, 360°$ — $\sin \theta = \frac{1}{2}$ or $\sin \theta = -\frac{1}{2}$.

$\sin \theta = \frac{1}{2} \Rightarrow \theta = 30°, 150°$ — 1 — If you solve $1 - 4 \sin^2\theta = 0$ by

$\sin \theta = -\frac{1}{2} \Rightarrow \theta = 210°, 330°$ — 1 — writing it as $\sin^2\theta = \frac{1}{4}$ you may

$\underline{\theta = 0, 30°, 150°, 180°, 210°, 330°, 360°}$ — forget that there are two square roots.

Answer	Mark	Examiner's tip

8 (a) $f(x) = \cos x° - \tan x°$

Now $\cos x°$ is defined for all values of x in the range –180 to 360, but $\tan x°$ is not defined when $x = -90, 90$ or 270

∴ $f(x)$ is not defined for $x = \pm 90,\ 270$ **1**

Knowledge of the basic trigonometric curves is required.

(b)

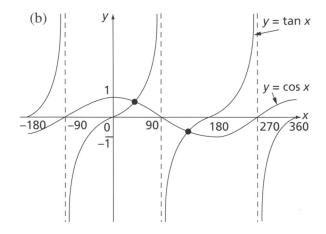

If you are using your graphics calculator, choose a suitable scale.

Show the scale on the x-axis, labelling the points where the curve cross it.   **1**

(c)   Now $f(x) = 0$ when $\cos x° - \tan x° = 0$

i.e. $\cos x° = \tan x°$

The values of x which satisfy this equation are given by the x coordinates of the points of intersection of the curves. From the sketch, we see that there are 2 roots.   **1**

You must justify your answer for the number of roots.

(d)   There is one root between 0 and 90, and another between 90 and 180.

Consider $f(x) = \cos x° - \tan x°$,

we want $f(x) = 0$

You need to use trial and improvement methods, homing in on the required values.

If you are using the trace facility on the calculator, you must show some working to justify your answers.

$f(30) = 0.288\ \ldots$ $f(120) = 1.23\ \ldots$

$f(40) = -0.073\ \ldots$ $f(130) = 0.54\ \ldots$

$f(35) = 0.118\ \ldots$ $f(140) = 0.07\ \ldots$

$f(38) = 0.006\ \ldots$ $f(150) = -0.288\ \ldots$

$f(39) = -0.03\ \ldots$ $f(141) = 0.03\ \ldots$

$f(142) = -0.006\ \ldots$

Look for a sign change. See Numerical methods, Unit 8.

Therefore   Therefore

$38 < x < 39$ $141 < x < 142$ **2**

Answer	Mark	Examiner's tip

9 $4\tan^2 x + 12\sec x + 1 = 0$

$4(\sec^2 x - 1) + 12\sec x + 1 = 0$ **1**

     $4\sec^2 x + 12\sec x - 3 = 0$ **1**

$$\sec x = \frac{-12 \pm \sqrt{144 - 4(4)(-3)}}{8}$$

$$= \frac{-12 \pm \sqrt{192}}{8}$$

$\therefore \ \sec x = -3.232\ldots \Rightarrow \cos x = -0.3094\ldots$

     $x = \pm 108°$ (nearest degree)   **2**

or $\sec x = 0.232\ldots \Rightarrow \cos x = 4.309\ldots$

     no possible solutions

$\therefore \ \underline{x = \pm 108°}$ **2**

Remember the relationship between sec x and tan x:
$1 + \tan^2 x = \sec^2 x.$

The quadratic formula is required here, since the equation does not factorise.

Give your answers in the range specified.

10 (a) $y = a + b\sin cx$

     $\underline{a = 2, \ b = 1, \ c = 2}$ **3**

  (b) $2 + \sin 2x = 2.5$

           $\sin 2x = 0.5$

In given range, $2x = \dfrac{\pi}{6}, \ \dfrac{5\pi}{6}$

      $\Rightarrow \underline{x = \dfrac{\pi}{12}, \ \dfrac{5\pi}{12}}$ **3**

'Write down' infers that you should be able to spot the values straight away. You do not need to put supporting reasons.
In fact $y = \sin x$ has been stretched by factor $\frac{1}{c}$ from $x = 0$, stretched by factor b from $y = 0$ and translated by $\begin{pmatrix} 0 \\ a \end{pmatrix}$ – see Unit 4, Functions.
Give your answers to (b) in terms of π.

6   DIFFERENTIATION

Answer	Mark	Examiner's tip

1 (a) $\dfrac{d}{dx}(3e^{2x}) = 6e^{2x}$ **1**

  (b) $\dfrac{d}{dx}(x^2\cos x) = x^2(-\sin x) + 2x\cos x$

             $= -x^2\sin x + 2x\cos x$ **2**

  (c) $\dfrac{d}{dx}\left(\dfrac{\sin x}{x}\right) = \dfrac{x\cos x - \sin x}{x^2}$ **2**

Differentiating a product:
$$\frac{d}{dx}(uv) = u\frac{dv}{dx} + v\frac{du}{dx}$$

Differentiating a quotient:
$$\frac{d}{dx}\left(\frac{u}{v}\right) = \frac{v\dfrac{du}{dx} - u\dfrac{dv}{dx}}{v^2}$$

Answer	Mark	Examiner's tip

2 $r = \dfrac{1+4t}{2+t}$

(a)   When $t = 0$, $r = \frac{1}{2}$ **1**   The expression 'initial' relates to $t = 0$. You need to realise this, otherwise it is difficult to progress.

    r is double its original value when $r = 1$

$$\Rightarrow 1 = \frac{1+4t}{2+t}$$ **1**

$$2 + t = 1 + 4t$$

$$3t = 1$$

$$t = \tfrac{1}{3}$$ **1**

<u>The radius doubles its initial value</u>

<u>in $\frac{1}{3}$ sec.</u>

(b) $\dfrac{dr}{dt} = \dfrac{(2+t)\,4 \;-\; (1+4t)\,1}{(2+t)^2}$ **2**   The rate of increase of the radius, in cm s^{-1}, is $\dfrac{dr}{dt}$. You need to use the quotient rule to find it.

$$= \frac{7}{(2+t)^2}$$

    When $t = 3$, $\dfrac{dr}{dt} = \dfrac{7}{25} = 0.28$ **1**

    <u>The rate of increase of the radius</u>   **2**   State your answer clearly, remembering the units, or you may lose marks.

    <u>when $t = 3$ is 0.28 cm s^{-1}.</u>

(c) $r = \dfrac{1+4t}{2+t} = \dfrac{\dfrac{1}{t}+4}{\dfrac{2}{t}+1}$ You need to change the form of the expression for r. You could divide to give $r = 4 - \dfrac{7}{t+2}$.

    As $t \to \infty$, $\dfrac{1}{t} \to 0$ $\therefore$ <u>$r \to 4$.</u>   **2**

3 $y = (4x + 3)^5$

$$\frac{dy}{dx} = 20(4x+3)^4$$ **2**   Use the chain rule.

    When $x = -\frac{1}{2}$, $\dfrac{dy}{dx} = 20(1)^4 = 20$ **1**   Find the gradient of the tangent at $(-\frac{1}{2}, 1)$.

    Equation of tangent at $(-\frac{1}{2}, 1)$:

$$y - 1 = 20(x - (-\tfrac{1}{2}))$$ **1**

$$\underline{y = 20x + 11}$$ **1**

Answer	Mark	Examiner's tip

4 $y = x + \dfrac{4}{x} = x + 4x^{-1}$

$\dfrac{dy}{dx} = 1 - 4x^{-2}$

$\qquad = 1 - \dfrac{4}{x^2}$ — 1

The first step is to rewrite the term $\dfrac{4}{x}$ as $4x^{-1}$ in order to apply the rule for differentiation. Often the need arises to change the form of some given information.

At stationary points, $\dfrac{dy}{dx} = 0$

so $1 - \dfrac{4}{x^2} = 0 \Rightarrow x^2 = 4$

$\qquad\qquad x = \pm\, 2$

When $x = 2$, $y = 2 + \frac{4}{2} = 4$ — 1

When $x = -2$, $y = -2 - \frac{4}{2} = -4$ — 1

Note that the question asks for stationary points; find more than one.

There are stationary points at

(2, 4) and (− 2, − 4).

Now $\dfrac{d^2y}{dx^2} = \dfrac{8}{x^3}$

When $x = 2$, $\dfrac{d^2y}{dx^2} > 0 \Rightarrow$ minimum point — 1

When $x = -2$, $\dfrac{d^2y}{dx^2} < 0 \Rightarrow$ maximum point — 1

You could consider y values near the point or consider the sign of $\dfrac{dy}{dx}$ near the point – but do not choose $x = 0$ since the function is undefined. Make your method clear and state your conclusions.

(2, 4) is a minimum point and

(−2, −4) is a maximum point.

Try plotting the curve on a graphic calculator to confirm your conclusions.

If y increases as x increases, then $\dfrac{dy}{dx} > 0$ — 1

i.e. $1 - \dfrac{4}{x^2} > 0 \Rightarrow 1 > \dfrac{4}{x^2} \Rightarrow x^2 > 4$

Take care with inequalities. It is possible to multiply by x^2 here, since $x^2 > 0$.

Do not forget negative values. In more complicated situations, sketch the function.

∴ $x < -2$ or $x > 2$ — 2

Answer	Mark	Examiner's tip

5 $y = 4x - x^2 \Rightarrow \dfrac{dy}{dx} = 4 - 2x$ — 1

When $x = 0$, $\dfrac{dy}{dx} = 4$ — 1

(graph: y axis, lines $y = 4x$, $y = x$, angles A and B at origin O; $\tan A = 4$, $\tan B = 1$)

— 1 — Remember that the gradient is given by the tan of the angle between the line and the positive x-axis.

$\tan(A - B) = \dfrac{\tan A - \tan B}{1 + \tan A \tan B}$

The required angle is $A - B$.

$\qquad = \dfrac{4 - 1}{1 + 4(1)} = 0.6$ — 2

$\therefore A - B = 31.0°$ (1 d.p.) — 1

Therefore the angle between the line

$y = x$ and the tangent is $31.0°$ (1 d.p.)

6 $\quad x = e^{2t} - 5t \qquad\qquad y = e^{2t} - 2t$

$\dfrac{dx}{dt} = 2e^{2t} - 5 \qquad\qquad \dfrac{dy}{dt} = 2e^{2t} - 2$ — 2

$\dfrac{dy}{dx} = \dfrac{dy}{dt} \times \dfrac{dt}{dx} \quad$ where $\dfrac{dt}{dx} = \dfrac{1}{dx/dt}$

$\dfrac{dy}{dx} = \dfrac{2e^{2t} - 2}{2e^{2t} - 5}$ — 1 — Do not be tempted to cancel anything here.

When gradient = 2,

$\dfrac{2e^{2t} - 2}{2e^{2t} - 5} = 2$ — 1

$2e^{2t} - 2 = 4e^{2t} - 10$

$2e^{2t} = 8$

$e^{2t} = 4$ — 1

$2t = \ln 4$

$t = \tfrac{1}{2} \ln 4$ — You are asked to find the *exact* value, so do not use a calculator.

$\quad = \ln 4^{1/2}$

$\quad = \underline{\ln 2}$ — 1

Answer	Mark	Examiner's tip

7 (a) $X = 500\, e^{-\frac{1}{5}t}$

$200 = 500\, e^{-\frac{1}{5}t} \Rightarrow e^{-\frac{1}{5}t} = \frac{200}{500} = 0.4$ (1)

$\qquad\qquad -\frac{1}{5}t = \ln 0.4$

$\qquad\qquad\quad t = -5 \ln 0.4$

$\qquad\qquad\qquad = 4.58\ \text{hr (2 d.p.)}$

Mark: 2, 1

Examiner's tip: Take logs to base e of both sides.

(b) (i) $\dfrac{\mathrm{d}X}{\mathrm{d}t} = -\frac{1}{5}\left(500\, e^{-\frac{1}{5}t}\right)$

$\qquad\quad = -100\, e^{-\frac{1}{5}t}$

Mark: 2

Examiner's tip: Notice that you have a value for $e^{-\frac{1}{5}t}$ from part (a). There is no need to substitute the value of t found in (a), but if you do, use the uncorrected value, *not* the 2 d.p. answer.

(ii) When $X = 200$, $e^{-\frac{1}{5}t} = 0.4$ from (1)

$\dfrac{\mathrm{d}X}{\mathrm{d}t} = -100 \times 0.4$

$\qquad = -40$

This indicates that X is decreasing, and the rate of decrease is 40 milligrammes per hour.

Mark: 1

8 $y = x^3 + bx^2 + cx$

(a) $\dfrac{\mathrm{d}y}{\mathrm{d}x} = 3x^2 + 2bx + c$

Mark: 2

(b) When $x = -1$ and $x = 3$, $\dfrac{\mathrm{d}y}{\mathrm{d}x} = 0$

$x = -1 \Rightarrow\quad 0 = 3 - 2b + c$ (1)

$x = 3 \ \Rightarrow\quad 0 = 27 + 6b + c$ (2)

$(2)-(1)\quad\ 0 = 24 + 8b$

$\qquad\qquad\quad b = -3$

Substitute in (1) $\underline{c = -9}$

Mark: 2, 1, 2

Examiner's tip: Explain how you are solving the simultaneous equations.

(c) $y = x^3 - 3x^2 - 9x$

When $x = -1$, $y = (-1)^3 - 3(-1)^2 - 9(-1) = 5$

When $x = 3$, $y = 3^3 - 3(3^2) - 9(3) = -27$

$\therefore$ The local maximum value of y is 5,

the local minimum value of y is -27.

Mark: 2

Answer	Mark	Examiner's tip

(d) A zero is where the function $y = f(x)$ intersects $y = 0$. The translated graph will have only one zero when <u>$d > 27$ or $d < -5$.</u>

2

You may find it helpful to draw sketches to explain your answers.

9 (a) $y = 2x^{-\frac{1}{3}} + x^{\frac{2}{3}}$

$\frac{dy}{dx} = \left(-\frac{1}{3}\right) 2x^{-\frac{4}{3}} + \frac{2}{3} x^{-\frac{1}{3}}$

3

At $x = 1$, $\frac{dy}{dx} = -\frac{2}{3} + \frac{2}{3} = 0$ as required

2

Take time to work out the indices properly, remembering that you need to reduce the power of x by 1 when differentiating.

(b) $A = \int y \, dx$

so $A = \int_1^8 \left(2x^{-\frac{1}{3}} + x^{\frac{2}{3}}\right) dx$

2

$= \left[\frac{2}{\frac{2}{3}} x^{\frac{2}{3}} + \frac{x^{\frac{5}{3}}}{\frac{5}{3}}\right]_1^8$

$= \left[3x^{\frac{2}{3}} + \frac{3}{5} x^{\frac{5}{3}}\right]_1^8$

3

$= 3(8)^{\frac{2}{3}} + \frac{3}{5}(8)^{\frac{5}{3}} - \left(3 + \frac{3}{5}\right)$

$= 27.6$

The area of R is 27.6 square units.

2

A common feature of calculus questions is to include differentiation and integration in the same question.
Be clear about each process.
When integrating, raise the power of x by 1.

For more practice see the integration questions.

7 INTEGRATION

Answer	Mark	Examiner's tip

1 (i) (a) $\int (2x + 3)^4 \, dx = \frac{1}{10} (2x + 3)^5 + c$

2

(b) $\int \left(1 + \frac{3}{4x}\right) dx = \int \left(1 + \frac{3}{4}\left(\frac{1}{x}\right)\right) dx$

$= x + \frac{3}{4} \ln |x| + c$

3

(ii) $\int 6\sqrt{x} \, dx = \int 6x^{\frac{1}{2}} \, dx$

$= \frac{6x^{\frac{3}{2}}}{\frac{3}{2}} + c$

$= 4x^{\frac{3}{2}} + c$

1

In general, $\int (ax + b)^n \, dx$

$= \frac{1}{a(n + 1)} (ax + b)^{n+1} + c$

Be careful with $\frac{3}{4}$.
Do not forget to include the constant.
Put $\sqrt{x}$ into index form.

Answer	Mark	Examiner's tip

$$\int_1^4 6\sqrt{x}\,dx = \left[4x^{\frac{3}{2}}\right]_1^4$$

1     $4^{\frac{3}{2}} = (\sqrt{4})^3 = 8$

$$= 32 - 4$$
$$= 28$$

1

2 (a) $\dfrac{d}{dx}\left(1+x^3\right)^{\frac{1}{2}} = \tfrac{1}{2}\left(1+x^3\right)^{-\frac{1}{2}} \times 3x^2$

Use the chain rule carefully.

$$= \dfrac{3x^2}{2\sqrt{1+x^3}}$$

3

(b) $\displaystyle\int_0^2 \dfrac{x^2}{\sqrt{1+x^3}}\,dx = \tfrac{2}{3}\left[\sqrt{1+x^3}\right]_0^2$

2   The wording of the question directs you to look for a relationship between the integral and the function just differentiated.

$$= \tfrac{2}{3}\left(\sqrt{9} - \sqrt{1}\right)$$
$$= \tfrac{4}{3}$$

2   A suitable substitution would be $1 + x^3 = u^2$.

3

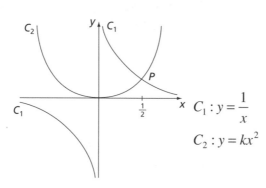

$C_1 : y = \dfrac{1}{x}$

$C_2 : y = kx^2$

It is a good idea to draw a sketch. Both curves are standard ones which you should know.

(a) At P, $\dfrac{1}{x} = kx^2$

1

$$\Rightarrow k = \dfrac{1}{x^3}$$

You are effectively solving two simultaneous equations.

Since $x = \tfrac{1}{2}$, $k = \dfrac{1}{\left(\tfrac{1}{2}\right)^3} = 8$

1

(b) $C_1 : y = x^{-1}$

$$\dfrac{dy}{dx} = -\dfrac{1}{x^2}$$

2   You need the gradient at a particular point, so substitute the x-value at that point.

At P, $x = \tfrac{1}{2} \Rightarrow \dfrac{dy}{dx} = -\dfrac{1}{\left(\tfrac{1}{2}\right)^2} = -4$

1

(c)

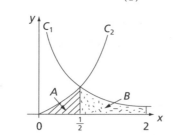

Find the required area in two parts. The sketch will help you to clarify which curve you need for each part and the limits required.

Answer	Mark	Examiner's tip

Area $A = \int_0^{\frac{1}{2}} 8x^2 \, dx$

$= \frac{8}{3}\left[x^3\right]_0^{\frac{1}{2}}$ 2

$= \underline{\frac{1}{3}}$ 2

Area $B = \int_{\frac{1}{2}}^{2} \frac{1}{x} \, dx$ 1

$= \left[\ln|x|\right]_{\frac{1}{2}}^{2}$ 1

$= \ln 2 - \ln \frac{1}{2}$

$= \ln 2 - \ln\left(2^{-1}\right)$

There is no need to find the area of B numerically until the final line.

$= 2 \ln 2$ 2

Total area $= \frac{1}{3} + 2 \ln 2$

$= \underline{1.72 \ (2 \text{ d.p.})}$ 2

Give the answer to the requested number of decimal places.

4 (a)

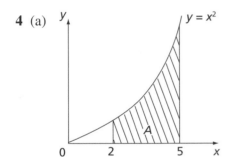

Note that you are instructed to draw a sketch; do not forget to do so.   1

Area $A = \int y \, dx$

$= \int_2^5 x^2 \, dx$

$= \left[\frac{x^3}{3}\right]_2^5$

$= \underline{39 \text{ square units}}$ 1

(b)

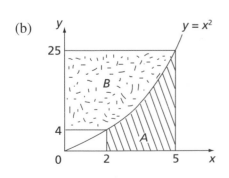

A clear diagram is essential here to explain your method.

Now $B = \int x \, dy$

To find area B, consider strips parallel to the x-axis and use

$= \int_4^{25} \sqrt{y} \, dy$ 1 $\int x \, dy$.

Answer	Mark	Examiner's tip

From the diagram

Area $B = 5 \times 25 -$ Area $A - 4 \times 2$

$\qquad = 125 - 39 - 8$

$\qquad = 78$ ... **1**

Therefore $\underline{\int_4^{25} \sqrt{y}\ \mathrm{d}y = 78}$

Examiner's tip: Be ready to think about the physical interpretation of the integral, which in this case is the area enclosed by the curve, the y-axis, $y = 4$ and $y = 25$. Note the firm instruction about relating part (b) to part (a).

(c)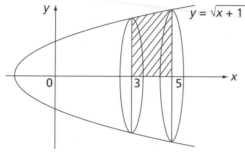

$V = \pi \int y^2\ \mathrm{d}x$

$\quad = \pi \int_3^5 (x+1)\ \mathrm{d}x$ ... **1**

$\quad = \pi \left[\tfrac{1}{2} x^2 + x \right]_3^5$

$\quad = \pi \left(\tfrac{25}{2} + 5 - \left(\tfrac{9}{2} + 3 \right) \right)$

$\quad = \underline{10\pi \text{ cubic units}}$ ... **1**

Examiner's tip: In (c) the graph is not essential, but useful.

Examiner's tip: Show the working for the substitution of the limits and leave your answer in terms of π.

5 (a) $\dfrac{\mathrm{d}}{\mathrm{d}x}(x \ln x) = x\left(\dfrac{1}{x}\right) + \ln x(1)$

$\qquad\qquad = 1 + \ln x$ ... **2**

There is a stationary point on the curve when $\ln x = -1$. i.e. $x = e^{-1}$ ... **1**

When $x = e^{-1}$, $y = e^{-1} \ln(e^{-1}) = -e^{-1}$

Now $\dfrac{\mathrm{d}^2 y}{\mathrm{d}x^2} = \dfrac{1}{x}$, so when $x = \dfrac{1}{e}$, $\dfrac{\mathrm{d}^2 y}{\mathrm{d}x^2} = e > 0$.

This implies that there is a minimum ... **1**

point at $\underline{\left(\dfrac{1}{e}, -\dfrac{1}{e} \right)}$. ... **1**

Examiner's tip: You will need to use the product rule.

Examiner's tip: You will lose marks if you do not justify that there is a minimum point.

Answer	Mark	Examiner's tip

(b)   Since $\dfrac{d^2y}{dx^2} = \dfrac{1}{x}$ and $x > 0$, $\dfrac{d^2y}{dx^2}$ is never

zero so the curve has no point of inflection.   **1**

At a point of inflection,

$$\dfrac{d^2y}{dx^2} = 0$$

(c)

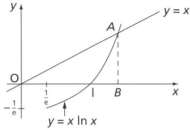

1

Use your calculator to sketch the curve, but you should know that when $x = 1$, $y = 0$ since $\ln 1 = 0$.

(d)   At A: $x \ln x = x$

Since $x > 0$, $\ln x = 1$

                  $x = e$ **1**

So A has coordinates (e, e)

Area $\Delta OAB = \frac{1}{2}e^2$

Area required $= \frac{1}{2}e^2 - \displaystyle\int_1^e x \ln x \, dx$

$= \frac{1}{2}e^2 - \displaystyle\int_1^e \ln x . x \, dx$

$= \frac{1}{2}e^2 - \left(\left[\ln x . \dfrac{x^2}{2} \right]_1^e - \displaystyle\int_1^e \dfrac{x^2}{2} . \dfrac{1}{x} \, dx \right)$ **2**

$= \frac{1}{2}e^2 - \frac{1}{2}e^2 + \frac{1}{2}\displaystyle\int_1^e x \, dx$

$= \frac{1}{4}\left[x^2 \right]_1^e$

$= \frac{1}{4}\left(e^2 - 1 \right)$ **2**

Use integration by parts

$$\int u \dfrac{dv}{dx} dx = uv - \int v \dfrac{du}{dx} dx$$

with $u = \ln x$; $\dfrac{dv}{dx} = x$

$\dfrac{du}{dx} = \dfrac{1}{x}$, $v = \frac{1}{2}x^2$

Remember that this is a special case. Do not try to take $u = x$.

6 (a) $\displaystyle\int x \cos x \, dx = x \sin x - \int \sin x . 1 \, dx$ **2**

                          $= x \sin x + \cos x + c$ **2**

Be aware that you must use integration by parts to integrate this product.

(b) $\displaystyle\int \cos^2 y \, dy = \frac{1}{2}\displaystyle\int (1 + \cos 2y) \, dy$ **1**

                  $= \frac{1}{2}\left(y + \frac{1}{2} \sin 2y \right) + c$

                  $= \frac{1}{2}y + \frac{1}{4} \sin 2y + k$ **3**

Remember the special technique of using double angles when integrating even powers of sin or cos.

Answer	Mark	Examiner's tip

$$\int \frac{1}{\sec^2 2y}\, \mathrm{d}y = \int x \cos x\, \mathrm{d}x$$

$$\Rightarrow \int \cos^2 2y\, \mathrm{d}y = \int x \cos x\, \mathrm{d}x \qquad 1$$

$$\tfrac{1}{2}\int (1 + \cos 4y)\, \mathrm{d}y = x \sin x + \cos x + c$$

$$\tfrac{1}{2}\left(y + \tfrac{1}{4}\sin 4y\right) = x \sin x + \cos x + c$$

$$\therefore\ \underline{y + \tfrac{1}{4}\sin 4y = 2(x \sin x + \cos x) + d} \qquad 3$$

Separate the variables carefully. Parts (a) and (b) have already prepared you for the integration of each side, but note that you must alter the format of $\dfrac{1}{\sec^2 2y}$ and then use a similar technique to part (b) to integrate it.

7 (a) We are given $\dfrac{\mathrm{d}R}{\mathrm{d}t} = -kR,\ k > 0$

$$\int \frac{1}{R}\, \mathrm{d}R = -k\int \mathrm{d}t$$

$$\ln R = -kt + c$$

$$\Rightarrow R = \mathrm{e}^{-kt+c} = \mathrm{e}^{-kt}.\mathrm{e}^{c} = A\mathrm{e}^{-kt}$$

Now when $t = 0$, $R = 10$, so $10 = A$

$$\therefore\ \underline{R = 10\mathrm{e}^{-kt}} \qquad 2$$

This is a very common differential equation and it is useful to be familiar with this form of the solution, in which the integration constant A is equal to the initial value of the variable, i.e. the value when $t = 0$.

(b) When $t = 1600$, $R = 5$

$$5 = 10\mathrm{e}^{-1600\,k} \qquad 1$$

$$\tfrac{1}{2} = \mathrm{e}^{-1600\,k}$$

$$2 = \mathrm{e}^{1600\,k}$$

$$\ln 2 = 1600\,k$$

$$\Rightarrow\ k = \frac{\ln 2}{1600} \qquad 1$$

$\tfrac{1}{2} = 2^{-1}$, so $2^{-1} = \mathrm{e}^{-1600k}$

$\Rightarrow 2 = \mathrm{e}^{1600k}$

Your method of working must be shown.

(c) When $t = 100$, $R = 10\mathrm{e}^{-\frac{\ln 2}{1600}(100)}$ \qquad 1

$$= \underline{9.58 \text{ grams } (2 \text{ d.p.})} \qquad 1$$

Again, show this line. If you just write down the numerical answer you will lose 2 marks.

8 (i) $\dfrac{\mathrm{d}r}{\mathrm{d}t} = k \Rightarrow r = kt + c \quad (k > 0)$

$$t = 0,\ r = 1 \Rightarrow 1 = c,\quad \therefore r = kt + 1$$

$$t = 10,\ r = 2 \Rightarrow 2 = 10k + 1,\quad \therefore k = 0.1$$

The model is $r = 0.1t + 1$, and the rate of increase is 0.1

$$t = T,\ r = 4 \Rightarrow 4 = 0.1T + 1$$

$$\underline{T = 30} \qquad 3$$

Do not forget to include the integration constant, then use the two conditions to find k and c; k gives the rate of increase.

Answer	Mark	Examiner's tip

(ii) $\dfrac{dr}{dt} = \dfrac{k}{r}$ — **1**

$\int r\,dr = \int k\,dt$ — **1** — Separate the variables and integrate both sides.

$\frac{1}{2}r^2 = kt + c$ — **2**

$t = 0,\ r = 1 \Rightarrow \frac{1}{2} = c \quad \therefore \frac{1}{2}r^2 = kt + \frac{1}{2}$ — **1**

$\qquad\qquad\qquad\qquad r^2 = 2kt + 1$

$t = 10,\ r = 2 \Rightarrow 4 = 20k + 1$

$\qquad\qquad k = 0.15$ — **2**

The model is $r^2 = 0.3t + 1$ — It helps to state the formula clearly, so that you can use it in the last part.

$t = T,\ r = 4 \Rightarrow 16 = 0.3T + 1$

$\qquad\qquad T = 50$ — **1**

9 Let $x = 2\cos\theta \Rightarrow \dfrac{dx}{d\theta} = -2\sin\theta$ — **1**

and $\sqrt{4 - x^2} = \sqrt{4 - 4\cos^2\theta} = 2\sin\theta$ — Change the limits to those of the new variable.

Limits: when $x = 1,\ \cos\theta = \frac{1}{2} \Rightarrow \theta = \dfrac{\pi}{3}$ — You should recognise the values of θ here and leave them as multiples of π.

when $x = \sqrt{2},\ \cos\theta = \dfrac{\sqrt{2}}{2} \Rightarrow \theta = \dfrac{\pi}{4}$ — **1**

$I = \displaystyle\int_{\frac{\pi}{3}}^{\frac{\pi}{4}} \dfrac{1}{4\cos^2\theta . 2\sin\theta} \cdot 2\sin\theta\ d\theta$ — Writing $\dfrac{1}{\cos^2\theta}$ as $\sec^2\theta$ leads to immediate recognition of the integral.

$= -\frac{1}{4}\displaystyle\int_{\frac{\pi}{3}}^{\frac{\pi}{4}} \sec^2\theta\ d\theta$ — **1**

$= -\frac{1}{4}\Big[\tan\theta\Big]_{\frac{\pi}{3}}^{\frac{\pi}{4}}$ — Learn the trig ratios of special angles, such as $\frac{\pi}{4}$ and $\frac{\pi}{3}$ so you can leave your answer in surd form as requested.

$= -\frac{1}{4}\left(1 - \sqrt{3}\right)$

$= \frac{1}{4}\left(\sqrt{3} - 1\right)$ — **2**

Answer	Mark	Examiner's tip

10 $\dfrac{d^2y}{dx^2} = 4$

$\dfrac{dy}{dx} = 4x + c$ **1**   Integrate with respect to x, then integrate again, but do not forget the constants.

$y = 2x^2 + cx + d$ **1**

When $x = 0$, $y = 3$ $\therefore 3 = d$ **1**   Use the given conditions to find the values of c and d.

When $x = 2$, $y = 5$ $\therefore 5 = 8 + 2c + 3$

$2c = -6$

$c = -3$

So $y = 2x^2 - 3x + 3$ **1**

11 (a) $x = 2t$ $y = t^2$

$\dfrac{dx}{dt} = 2$ $\dfrac{dy}{dt} = 2t$ **2**   Remember that $\dfrac{dt}{dx} = \dfrac{1}{dx/dt}$

$\dfrac{dy}{dx} = \dfrac{dy}{dt} \times \dfrac{dt}{dx}$

$= 2t \times \tfrac{1}{2}$

$= t$ **1**

When $t = 3$, $\dfrac{dy}{dx} = 3$ **1**

so gradient of normal $= -\tfrac{1}{3}$ **1**   Use $m_1 \times m_2 = -1$ for perpendicular lines.

When $t = 3$, $x = 2 \times 3 = 6$

$y = 3^2 = 9$

so P is the point $(6, 9)$.   **1**

Equation of normal at P: Use $y - y_1 = m(x - x_1)$

$y - 9 = -\tfrac{1}{3}(x - 6)$ **1**

$3y - 27 = -x + 6$

$3y + x = 33$ **1**

(b) For the curve C:

t	−3	−2	−1	0	1	2	3
x	−6	−4	−2	0	2	4	6
y	9	4	1	0	1	4	9

For the line:

x	0	3	6
y	11	10	9

To sketch the curve, work out a few points for various values of t, or find the cartesian equation of C which is in fact needed for part (c) of the question.

Region *R* is shaded.

B

11

P

(6, 9)

y

O

x

2

Answer	Mark	Examiner's tip

(c) Cartesian equation of C:

$t = \dfrac{x}{2}, y = t^2 \Rightarrow y = \left(\dfrac{x}{2}\right)^2$ i.e. $4y = x^2$ — **1**

$V = \pi \displaystyle\int_0^9 4y \, dy + \pi \int_9^{11} (33 - 3y)^2 \, dy$ — **2**

$\quad = \pi \left[2y^2\right]_0^9 + \pi \left[-\tfrac{1}{9}(33 - 3y)^3\right]_9^{11}$ — **2**

$\quad = 162\pi + \pi\,(0 - (-\tfrac{1}{9} \times 6^3))$

$\quad = 162\pi + 24\pi$

$\quad = \underline{186\pi}$ cubic units — **2**

Use $V = \pi \displaystyle\int x^2 \, dy$ considering the two different sections from $y = 0$ to $y = 9$ and from $y = 9$ to $y = 11$.

To integrate $(33 - 3y)^2$ you could expand the expression and integrate term by term:

$\pi \displaystyle\int_9^{11} (33 - 3y)^2 \, dy$

$= \pi \displaystyle\int_9^{11} (1089 - 198y + 9y^2) \, dy$

$= \pi \left[1089y - 99y^2 + 3y^3\right]_9^{11} = 24\pi$

12 (a) Acceleration $= \dfrac{dv}{dt}$

$v = 3t^2 + 1$

$\dfrac{dv}{dt} = 6t$ — **1**

When $t = 4$, $\dfrac{dv}{dt} = 24$ — **1**

The acceleration is $\underline{24 \text{ ms}^{-2}}$.

Remember the relationship between displacement, velocity and acceleration.

(b) $s = \displaystyle\int_0^4 v \, dt$

$\quad = \displaystyle\int_0^4 (3t^2 + 1) \, dt$ — **1**

$\quad = \left[t^3 + t\right]_0^4$ — **1**

$\quad = 68$ — **1**

The displacement is $\underline{68 \text{ m}}$.

13 $\qquad y = \ln(1 + x) \qquad\qquad y = x - \tfrac{1}{2}x^2$

$\dfrac{dy}{dx} = \dfrac{1}{1 + x} \qquad\qquad \dfrac{dy}{dx} = 1 - x$ — **2**

When $x = 0.2$, $\qquad\qquad$ When $x = 0.2$,

$\dfrac{dy}{dx} = \dfrac{1}{1.2} \qquad\qquad\quad \dfrac{dy}{dx} = 1 - 0.2$

$\qquad = \underline{0.8\dot{3}} \qquad\qquad\qquad\quad = \underline{0.8}$ — **1**

(i) $\displaystyle\int_0^{0.2} (x - \tfrac{1}{2}x^2) \, dx = \left[\tfrac{1}{2}x^2 - \tfrac{1}{6}x^3\right]_0^{0.2}$ — **1**

$\qquad\qquad\qquad = \underline{0.0187}$ (4 d.p.) — **1**

Follow the instructions about degree of accuracy.

Answer	Mark	Examiner's tip
(ii)　　$y = \ln(1 + x)$ 　　　　$e^y = 1 + x$ 　　　　$x = e^y - 1$	2	Write this in index form.
Area $J = \displaystyle\int_0^{\ln 1.2} x \, \mathrm{d}y$		Leave the limit in its *exact* form of $\ln 1.2$.
$= \displaystyle\int_0^{\ln 1.2} (e^y - 1) \, \mathrm{d}y$	1	
$= \left[e^y - y \right]_0^{\ln 1.2}$	1	
$= 1.2 - \ln 1.2 - 1$		Remember that $e^{\ln x} = x$ and $e^0 = 1$.
$= 0.2 - \ln 1.2$	1	Note that the *exact* area is required. Do not use a calculator in this part.
Area $I + J = 0.2 \times \ln 1.2$ $\therefore$ Area $I = 0.2 \ln 1.2 - (0.2 - \ln 1.2)$	1	Use brackets.
$= 0.0188$ (4 d.p.)	1	

8 NUMERICAL METHODS

Answer	Mark	Examiner's tip
1 Using $x_{n+1} = 2(1+e^{-x_n})$, $x_1 = 0$ gives		
$x_2 = 2(1+e^0) = 4$	1	Show sufficient working, for the first few iterations, to illustrate use of the iteration formula.
$x_3 = 2(1+e^{-4}) = 2.03663...$		
Continuing in the same way gives		List the results of the later iterations without showing all the working.
$x_4 = 2.260\,93...$		
$x_5 = 2.208\,50...$		
$x_6 = 2.219\,72...$		A graphic calculator is very well suited to this process. e.g. Try
$x_7 = 2.217\,27...$		$0 \rightarrow X$
$x_8 = 2.217\,81...$		$2(1 + e^{-X}) \rightarrow X$
$x_9 = 2.217\,69...$		
$x_{10} = 2.217\,71...$	1	Continue until you are confident that there there will be no further changes that will affect the third decimal place.
$x_{11} = 2.217\,71...$		
$\therefore \alpha = 2.218$ correct to 3 decimal places.	1	
An equation of which α is a root is $x = 2(1 + e^{-x})$	1	

Answer	Mark	Examiner's tip

2 (a) $x^3 + 3x^2 - 7 = 0 \Rightarrow x^2(x+3) - 7 = 0$

$\Rightarrow x^2 = \dfrac{7}{x+3} \Rightarrow x = \sqrt{\dfrac{7}{x+3}}$

The fact that the rearranged form involves taking the $\sqrt{}$ at the final stage suggests that we need to isolate a quadratic factor.

(assuming $x > 0$)   **1**

Hence $\underline{a = 7}$ and $\underline{b = 3}$ **1**

(b) Taking $x_0 = 2$,

$x_1 = \sqrt{\dfrac{7}{5}} = 1.18321....$ **1**

Continuing in the same way,

$x_2 = 1.293\ 58...$ **1**

$x_3 = 1.276\ 84...$

$x_4 = 1.279\ 34...$ **1**

The approximate solution given by x_4 is $\underline{1.28}$. Comparing the values of   **1**

x_2, x_3 and x_4 it appears that the the third decimal place is settling to a figure which will round off to 8.   **1**

Note:
In this case, the graph of $y = x^3 + 3x^2 - 7$ shows that the only real solution of $x^3 + 3x^2 - 7 = 0$ is positive. In cases where negative solutions exist it is necessary to consider a rearrangement of the form $x = -\sqrt{g(x)}$.

3 Let $f(x) = x^3 - x^2 - 2$

then $f(1) = -2 < 0$ and $f(2) = 2 > 0$ **2**

and so $f(x) = 0$ has a root α between 1 and 2.

It simply needs to be established that there is a change of sign in the value of $f(x)$.

(a) Using $x_{n+1} = x_n - \dfrac{f(x_n)}{f'(x_n)}$ gives

$x_{n+1} = x_n - \dfrac{x_n^3 - x_n^2 - 2}{3x_n^2 - 2x_n}$ **2**

Taking $x_1 = 1.5$ gives

$x_2 = 1.5 - \dfrac{1.5^3 - 1.5^2 - 2}{3 \times 1.5^2 - 2 \times 1.5}$ **1**

so the second approximation is $\underline{1.733}$ (to 3 d.p.)   **1**

(b) $x^3 - x^2 - 2 = 0 \Rightarrow x^3 = x^2 + 2$

$\Rightarrow x = \sqrt[3]{(x^2 + 2)}$ **2**

Taking $x_{n+1} = \sqrt[3]{(x_n^2 + 2)}$, $x_1 = 1.5$ gives   **1**

$x_2 = \sqrt[3]{(1.5^2 + 2)} = \underline{1.620}$ (to 3 d.p.)   **1**

$x_3 = \underline{1.666}$ (to 3 d.p.)   **1**

The values of the approximations found in parts (a) and (b) are different simply because the process has not been continued long enough for the results to converge. After several more iterations both processes converge to 1.695 620 8 to seven decimal places.

Answer	Mark	Examiner's tip

4 (a) $f(x) = e^x - 5x \Rightarrow f'(x) = e^x - 5$ ⟶ 3

(b) $f'(x) = 0 \Rightarrow e^x = 5 \Rightarrow x = \ln 5$ ⟶ 2

giving $\underline{x = 1.61}$ to 2 decimal places. ⟶ 1

(c) $f(0.2) = 0.221... > 0$, $f(0.3) = -0.150... < 0$. ⟶ 1

The change of sign shows that there is a root α of $f(x) = 0$ such that $0.2 < \alpha < 0.3$. ⟶ 1

(d) By inspection

$f(2.5) = -0.317... < 0$

$f(2.6) = 0.463... > 0$ ⟶ 2

and so $2.5 < \beta < 2.6$

$\underline{\therefore p = 25}$ ⟶ 2

Given that p is an integer it follows that $\dfrac{p}{10}$ contains one decimal place. This suggests that we should, first, determine β to 1 d.p. and then interpret the result in terms of p.

It is perfectly valid to locate β by drawing the graph of $y = f(x)$, using a graphics calculator, and then using the Trace function.

5 (a)

$x^2 + e^x - 4 = 0$ ⟶ 1

$\Rightarrow e^x = 4 - x^2$

i.e. All roots of the equation are found at the intersections of the graphs in the diagram, showing that $\underline{x^2 + e^x - 4 = 0 \text{ has one positive}}$ $\underline{\text{root and one negative root.}}$ ⟶ 1

Your sketch *must* be sufficiently accurate to allow you to establish the nature of the roots. ⟶ 2

You may prefer to start with $e^x = 4 - x^2$, representing the points where the curves intersect, and show this can be put in the form $x^2 + e^x - 4 = 0$. The important thing is to give a clearly reasoned argument.

(b) $x_1 = -1.965\,875\,051$

$x_2 = -1.964\,679\,797$

$x_3 = -1.964\,637\,175$ ⟶ 2

$x_4 = -1.964\,635\,654$

Value of root is -1.9646 correct to 4 d.p. ⟶ 1

(c) $x_1 = 0.575\,068\,111\,1$

$x_2 = 1.490\,888\,469$ ⟶ 1

x_3 is not a real number ⟶ 1

(the calculator displays an error message).

The process fails to locate the positive root because the expression inside the square root becomes negative. ⟶ 2

Answer	Mark	Examiner's tip

6

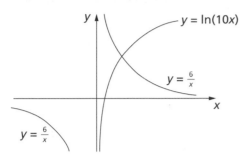

A graphics calculator may be helpful to sketch the graphs but take care to select appropriate Range values.

2

The graphs can only intersect on their common domain i.e. where $x > 0$. In this region $\frac{6}{x}$ is decreasing whereas $\ln(10x)$ is increasing. It follows that the equation $\ln(10x) = \frac{6}{x}$ has exactly one real root. **1**

Taking $x_0 = 2$, $x_1 = \dfrac{6}{\ln(20)} = 2.002\ 84...$ **1**

In the same way
$x_2 = 2.001\ 89...$
$x_3 = 2.002\ 21...$
$x_4 = 2.002\ 10...$
$x_5 = 2.002\ 14...$

Using a graphics calculator, try

$2 \rightarrow X$
$6 \div \ln(10X) \rightarrow X$

The solution is <u>2.002</u> (correct to 3 d.p.) **1**

Taking $f(x) = x\ln(10x) - 6$ gives

$f'(x) = x\left(\dfrac{1}{10x} \times 10\right) + \ln(10x) = 1 + \ln(10x)$ **2**

The differentiation requires the combined use of the product rule and the chain rule.

Using the Newton–Raphson result

$x_{n+1} = x_n - \dfrac{f(x_n)}{f'(x_n)}$

gives $x_{n+1} = x_n - \dfrac{x_n \ln(10x_n) - 6}{1 + \ln(10x_n)}$ **1**

$= \dfrac{x_n(1 + \ln(10x_n)) - x_n \ln(10x_n) + 6}{1 + \ln(10x_n)}$ **1**

$\therefore x_{n+1} = \dfrac{x_n + 6}{1 + \ln(10x_n)}$ **1**

The required simplification is achieved by using $1 + \ln(10x_n)$ as a common denominator.

7 (a) Shaded area $= \dfrac{r^2\theta}{2} - \dfrac{r^2\sin\theta}{2} = \dfrac{r^2}{2}(\theta - \sin\theta)$ **3**

Since θ is in radians, the area of the sector is $\dfrac{r^2\theta}{2}$.

(b) From given result

$\dfrac{r^2}{2}(\theta - \sin\theta) = \dfrac{\pi r^2}{6} \Rightarrow \theta - \sin\theta = \dfrac{\pi}{3}$

$\sin\theta = \theta - \dfrac{\pi}{3}$ **1**

Answer	Mark	Examiner's tip

(c)

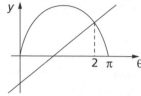

The point of intersection is close to 2 which verifies that $\theta = 2$ is an approximate

solution of $\sin\theta = \theta - \dfrac{\pi}{3}$ **1**

1 (top) — The sketch needs to be sufficiently accurate, and the horizontal scale sufficiently detailed, to verify the given result.

If you use a calculator make sure that it is set to work in radians.

(d) $\sin\theta = \theta - \dfrac{\pi}{3} \Rightarrow \sin\theta - \theta + \dfrac{\pi}{3} = 0$

Let $f(\theta) = \sin\theta - \theta + \dfrac{\pi}{3}$ then $f'(\theta) = \cos\theta - 1$ **1**

Using Newton's rule a better approximation

is given by $2 - \dfrac{\sin(2) - 2 + \dfrac{\pi}{3}}{\cos(2) - 1} = \underline{1.97 \text{ (2 d.p.)}}$ **2**

9 MATHEMATICS OF UNCERTAINTY

Answer	Mark	Examiner's tip

1 (a)

Weight of fish (x lb)	Class width	Frequency	Frequency density
$0 \le x < 1$	1	21	21
$1 \le x < 1.5$	0.5	32	64
$1.5 \le x < 2.0$	0.5	33	66
$2.0 \le x < 2.5$	0.5	24	48
$2.5 \le x < 3$	0.5	18	36
$3 \le x < 4$	1	21	21
$4 \le x < 5$	1	16	16
$5 \le x < 6$	1	12	12
$6 \le x < 8$	2	11	5.5
$8 \le x < 13$	5	12	2.4

2

You cannot just take the height of the bar to be the frequency, since the intervals are not equal.

Take time to work out the correct boundary points and frequency densities, where

$$\text{frequency density} = \frac{\text{frequency}}{\text{class width}}$$

Writing out the table helps you to clarify your thoughts.

Include all labelling, together with a heading, or you may lose marks.

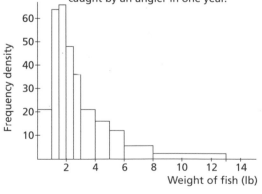

A histogram to show weights of fish caught by an angler in one year.

2

Answer	Mark	Examiner's tip

(b) Mean $\bar{x} = \dfrac{\Sigma fx}{\Sigma f}$, taking x as mid-class value

$$= \frac{626.25}{200}$$

$$= 3.13 \text{ lb (2 d.p.)} \qquad 1$$

Use the statistical functions on your calculator, although it is a good idea to note the key values in your working, rather than just presenting the final answers.

Standard deviation $= \sqrt{\dfrac{\Sigma fx^2}{\Sigma f} - \bar{x}^2}$

$$= \sqrt{\frac{3220.1875}{200} - \bar{x}^2}$$

$$= 2.51 \text{ lb (2 d.p.)} \qquad 2$$

Include the units in your final answers.

2 (a) (i) Cumulative frequency table

Speed	≤10	≤20	≤25	≤30	≤35	≤40	≤50	≤70
Cumulative frequency	0	18	44	134	192	224	242	250

2

A common mistake is to plot the cumulative frequencies against mid-points. Remember that upper class boundaries are needed.

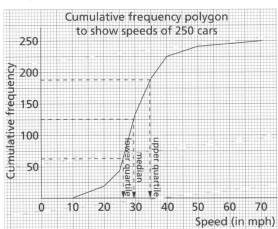

3

The points can be joined with straight lines to form a cumulative frequency polygon, or with a curve.

Label the axes and give a heading.

(ii) $n = 250$, so

median = 125th value = 29.5 mph
lower quartile = 62.5th value = 26 mph
upper quartile = 187.5th value = 34.5 mph   3

There will be slight variations in these values, depending on how you joined your points. It is advisable to show your working on your graph.

(b) (i) The extremes of the whiskers are at 10 and 70.

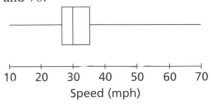

2

The box plot can be drawn horizontally or vertically. You could place it underneath your curve, using the same horizontal scale.

(ii) About half the vehicles break the speed limit, with one quarter breaking it by more than 5 mph. The whisker extends to 70 mph, indicating that some drivers are travelling at over twice the legal speed.   2

Try to make at least two points here.

Answer	Mark	Examiner's tip

3 (i) (a) It would be difficult to draw a histogram because it could not convey accurately such vastly different interval widths and column heights. — **2**

Examiner's tip: Two marks have been allocated, so try to pick out at least two points. You could think of other representations such as a pie chart!

(b) The last class is open-ended and although there are not many share-holders in this category, the size of the shareholding is so large that the total from it would make a significant contribution to the calculation of the mean. — **1**

(ii) The median is the $\frac{1}{2}$ (636 990)th reading, i.e. the 318 495th reading, which lies in the interval 100–499. — **1**

Taking the boundary points as 100 and 500 and noting that 318 495 – 133 853 = 184 642

the median is $\dfrac{184\ 642}{347\ 495}$ along this interval

$$\text{median} = 100 + \left(\dfrac{184\ 642}{347\ 495}\right) \times 400$$

$$= 312.5\ldots$$

So median size of shareholding approximately £310. — **2**

Examiner's tip: With such large numbers, it is essential to keep a clear head when deciding which numbers are required. You could use a graphical method, drawing the start of a cumulative frequency curve.

Explain your reasoning.

4 $p(A) = 0.4$, $p(B) = 0.7$, $p(A \text{ or } B) = 0.8$

(a) $p(A \text{ or } B) = p(A) + p(B) - p(A \text{ and } B)$
$0.8 = 0.4 + 0.7 - p(A \text{ and } B)$
$\Rightarrow \underline{p(A \text{ and } B) = 0.3}$ — **2**

Examiner's tip: This is a straightforward application of the probability laws.

(b) $p(A|B) = \dfrac{p(A \text{ and } B)}{p(B)} = \dfrac{0.3}{0.7} = \frac{3}{7}$ — **2**

5

P (V and P) = 0.003 × 0.95 = 0.00285

P ($\bar{V}$ and P) = 0.997 × 0.02 = 0.01994 — **4**

$P(\text{Positive result}) = 0.002\ 85 + 0.019\ 94$
$= 0.022\ 79$ — **2**

$P(V|P) = \dfrac{P(V \text{ and } P)}{P(P)} = \dfrac{0.002\ 85}{0.022\ 79} = \underline{0.125}$ (3 s.f.) — **2**

Examiner's tip: The easiest way to illustrate the given information is to draw a tree diagram and fill in the missing probabilities.
Note that these 4 marks are allocated as follows:
1 using tree
1 first set of branches
1 second set of branches
1 multiplying the probabilities.
It is helpful if you indicate on your diagram where the values come from.

Answer	Mark	Examiner's tip

6 (a)

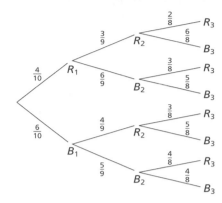

1

You may find it helpful to introduce the notation R_1, R_2, R_3, B_1, B_2, B_3 in the tree diagram.

1

Keep a clear head when filling in the probabilities, remembering how many of each colour are in the bag at each junction.

1

Each pair of branches must have probabilities adding up to 1.

1

It is better not to cancel any fractions in the tree.

Multiply probabilities as you go along the branches.

(b) $P(R_1 B_2 \text{ or } B_1 R_2) = \frac{4}{10} \times \frac{6}{9} + \frac{6}{10} \times \frac{4}{9}$

$$= \frac{8}{15}$$

2

(c) $P(R_3) = \frac{4}{10} \times \frac{3}{9} \times \frac{2}{8} + \frac{4}{10} \times \frac{6}{9} \times \frac{3}{8} + \frac{6}{10} \times \frac{4}{9} \times \frac{3}{8} + \frac{6}{10} \times \frac{5}{9} \times \frac{4}{8}$

2

$$= \frac{2}{5}$$

1

Note how the use of R_1, B_1, etc. provides a concise way of referring to the given events.

(d) $P(R_3 | B_1 B_2) = \dfrac{P(R_3 B_1 B_2)}{P(B_1 B_2)}$

$$= \frac{\frac{6}{10} \times \frac{5}{9} \times \frac{4}{8}}{\frac{6}{10} \times \frac{5}{9}}$$

1

$$= \frac{4}{8} = \frac{1}{2}$$

1

This can be seen directly, since if the first two balls are blue, there are 4 red balls out of the 8 left in the bag.

7 (a) Use the mid-points (x) to represent the intervals.

x	80	87.5	92.5	97.5	102.5	107.5	115
f	7	32	55	47	33	18	8

$$\bar{x} = \frac{\sum fx}{\sum f}$$

$$= \frac{19\,267.5}{200} = \underline{96.3 \text{ cm (1 d.p.)}}$$

1

Remember that mid-point $= \frac{1}{2}(\text{u.c.b.} + \text{l.c.b.})$

Take care when calculating the mid-points, noticing that the intervals are not of equal width.

$$(\text{s.d.})^2 = \frac{\sum fx^2}{\sum f} - \bar{x}^2$$

$$= \frac{1\,867\,706.3}{200} - \left(\frac{19\,267.5}{200}\right)^2$$

$$= 57.61\ldots$$

s.d. $= \underline{7.59 \text{ cm (2 d.p.)}}$

3

Even when using a calculator in SD mode, it is advisable to show the values used in the formulas. These can be obtained from the calculator.

(b) Since the intervals are not of equal width, the frequency densities are needed for the histogram.

$$\text{Frequency density} = \frac{\text{frequency}}{\text{interval width}}$$

They are 0.7, 6.4, 11, 9.4, 6.6, 3.6, 0.8

2

State the frequency densities.

Answer	Mark	Examiner's tip

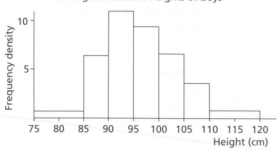

Histogram to show heights of boys

| | 2 | Remember to label your axes and give headings. |

8 (i) P(faulty and passes both stages)
$$= 0.4 \times 0.1 \times 0.1 = \underline{0.004}$$
Mark: 2

(ii) P(passes both stages) $= 0.004 + 0.6$
$$= \underline{0.604}$$
Mark: 2

(iii) P(faulty|passes both stages)

$$= \frac{P(\text{faulty and passes both stages})}{P(\text{passes both stages})}$$

$$= \frac{0.004}{0.604} = \frac{1}{\underline{151}}$$
Mark: 2

You will need to use

$$P(A|B) = \frac{P(A \text{ and } B)}{P(B)}$$

9 (i) (a) 8   (b) $n(5) = n(\le 5) - n(\le 4)$
$$= 8 - 3 = \underline{5}$$
Mark: 2

(ii)

Marks	3	4	5	6	7	8	9	10
Frequency	1	2	5	3	6	4	6	5

Mark: 3

Check that the total frequency is 32.

(iii) $$\bar{x} = \frac{\sum fx}{\sum f} = \frac{232}{32}$$
$$= \underline{7.25 \text{ marks}}$$
Mark: 1

It is useful to show the formulas and the totals in your working.

$$(\text{s.d.})^2 = \frac{\sum fx^2}{\sum f} = \frac{1810}{32} - (7.25)^2 = 4$$
$$\underline{\text{s.d.} = 2 \text{ marks}}$$
Mark: 2

If you use a calculator in SD mode and make a mistake, you will get no marks if there is no working.

10 VECTORS

Answer	Mark	Examiner's tip

1 $\mathbf{a} = 2\mathbf{i} - \mathbf{k}, \quad \mathbf{b} = \mathbf{i} + 2\mathbf{j} + \mathbf{k}, \quad \mathbf{c} = -\mathbf{j} + \mathbf{k}$
Mark: 3

(a) $\mathbf{a.b} + \mathbf{a.c} = (2 + 0 - 1) + (0 + 0 - 1) = \underline{0}$
Mark: 1

(b) $\mathbf{a.b} + \mathbf{a.c} = \mathbf{a.(b + c)}$

$\therefore \mathbf{a.(b + c)} = 0$

Since $|\mathbf{a}| \ne 0$ and $|\mathbf{b + c}| \ne 0$ it follows that

$\underline{\mathbf{b + c} \text{ is perpendicular to } \mathbf{a}.}$
Mark: 1

The scalar product is distributive over vector addition. In other words, the common factor $\mathbf{a}$ can be taken outside the brackets in the usual way.

Answer	Mark	Examiner's tip

2 (i) $\overrightarrow{ON} = \overrightarrow{OC} + \overrightarrow{CG} + \overrightarrow{GN}$ 1

$= 2\mathbf{j} + 2\mathbf{k} + \mathbf{i}$

$= \mathbf{i} + 2\mathbf{j} + 2\mathbf{k}$ 1

$\overrightarrow{MG} = \overrightarrow{MB} + \overrightarrow{BF} + \overrightarrow{FG}$

$= \mathbf{j} + 2\mathbf{k} - 2\mathbf{i}$

$= -2\mathbf{i} + \mathbf{j} + 2\mathbf{k}$ 1

Show sufficient working to make your method clear.
Note that any 'route' which starts at O and finishes at N will be equivalent in vector terms.

(ii) $\overrightarrow{ON} \cdot \overrightarrow{MG} = (\mathbf{i} + 2\mathbf{j} + 2\mathbf{k}) \cdot (-2\mathbf{i} + \mathbf{j} + 2\mathbf{k})$

$= -2 + 2 + 4 = 4$ 1

but $\overrightarrow{ON} \cdot \overrightarrow{MG} = ON \times MG \cos\theta$ 1

$= \sqrt{1^2 + 2^2 + 2^2} \times \sqrt{(-2)^2 + 1^2 + 2^2} \times \cos\theta$

$= 9\cos\theta$ 1

so $9\cos\theta = 4$

giving $\theta = \cos^{-1}\left(\frac{4}{9}\right) = 63.612...°$ 1

and so the acute angle between the directions of $\overrightarrow{ON}$ and $\overrightarrow{MG}$ is $63.6°$, correct to the nearest $0.1°$.   1

Note the distinction between, for example, the vector $\overrightarrow{ON}$ and the distance (scalar) ON.

Alternatively, you could use the formula $\theta = \cos^{-1}\left(\dfrac{\mathbf{a.b}}{|\mathbf{a}||\mathbf{b}|}\right)$

Interpret the calculated value of θ in terms of the original problem.

3 (a) **r** and **s** are perpendicular $\Rightarrow \mathbf{r.s} = 0$ 1

$(\lambda\mathbf{i} + (2\lambda - 1)\mathbf{j} - \mathbf{k}) \cdot ((1 - \lambda)\mathbf{i} + 3\lambda\mathbf{j} +$

$(4\lambda - 1)\mathbf{k}) = 0$ 1

$\lambda(1 - \lambda) + 3\lambda(2\lambda - 1) - (4\lambda - 1) = 0$ 2

$\lambda - \lambda^2 + 6\lambda^2 - 3\lambda - 4\lambda + 1 = 0$

$5\lambda^2 - 6\lambda + 1 = 0$ 1

$(5\lambda - 1)(\lambda - 1) = 0$

The values of λ for which **r** and **s** are perpendicular are <u>0.2 and 1</u>   2

Make a clear statement and substitute the given information.

Use brackets and take care with the negatives.

The fact that the quadratic factorises suggests that the working is correct but, time permitting, the result could easily be checked by substituting for λ in **r** and **s**.

(b) substituting $\lambda = 2$ gives

$\overrightarrow{OA} = 2\mathbf{i} + 3\mathbf{j} - \mathbf{k}$, $\overrightarrow{OB} = -\mathbf{i} + 6\mathbf{j} + 7\mathbf{k}$ 1

$\overrightarrow{AB} = \overrightarrow{OB} - \overrightarrow{OA}$

$= -\mathbf{i} + 6\mathbf{j} + 7\mathbf{k} - (2\mathbf{i} + 3\mathbf{j} - \mathbf{k})$

$= -3\mathbf{i} + 3\mathbf{j} + 8\mathbf{k}$ 1

Answer	Mark	Examiner's tip

(c)

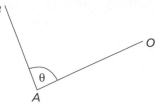

Angle *BAO* is the angle between the vectors $\overrightarrow{AB}$ and $\overrightarrow{AO}$. | 1 | An important statement.

$$\overrightarrow{AB}.\overrightarrow{AO} = (-3\mathbf{i}+3\mathbf{j}+8\mathbf{k}).(-2\mathbf{i}-3\mathbf{j}+\mathbf{k})$$

$$= 6 - 9 + 8 = 5$$ | 1 |

but

$$\overrightarrow{AB}.\overrightarrow{AO} = AB \times AO\cos\theta$$ | | Make your method clear by showing all of the necessary working.

$$= \sqrt{(-3)^2+3^2+8^2} \times \sqrt{(-2)^2+(-3)^2+1^2} \times \cos\theta$$ | 1 |

$$= \sqrt{82} \times \sqrt{14}\cos\theta$$

and so $\cos\theta = \dfrac{5}{\sqrt{82\times14}}$ | 1 |

giving $\theta = \cos^{-1}\left(\dfrac{5}{\sqrt{82\times14}}\right) = 81.51...°$

hence, <u>angle *BAO* = 82°</u> to the nearest degree. | 1 | Give the final answer to the required level of accuracy.

4 (a) (i) For the lines to intersect, there must be some value of *s* and *t* such that

$$2\mathbf{i}+s(\mathbf{i}+3\mathbf{j}+4\mathbf{k}) = \mathbf{k}+t(\mathbf{i}+\mathbf{j}+\mathbf{k})$$ | 1 |

Equating corresponding components gives

$2 + s = t$ (1) | | The single vector equation gives three separate equations in the two parameters *s* and *t*. All three equations must be stated.

$3s = t$ (2) | 1 |

$4s = t + 1$ (3)

From (1) and (2) $3s = 2+s \Rightarrow s = 1$

Substituting for *s* in (1) gives $t = 3$ | 1 | A value for *s* and *t* may be found using any pair of equations.

Checking for consistency in (3) gives

L.H.S. $= 4\times1 = 4$, R.H.S. $= 3+1 = 4$.

Since L.H.S. = R.H.S it follows that the equations are consistent and so the lines intersect. | 1 | To establish that the lines intersect, the values of *s* and *t* must be substituted in the remaining equation in order to check that the three equations are **consistent**. Avoid presenting a chain of reasoning which concludes that $4 = 4$.

Substituting $s = 1$ in the equation for *l* gives the position vector of the point of intersection as

$$3\mathbf{i}+3\mathbf{j}+4\mathbf{k}$$ | 1 |

Answer	Mark	Examiner's tip

(ii) The angle between the lines is given by the angle betwen the vectors
$\mathbf{i}+3\mathbf{j}+4\mathbf{k}$ and $\mathbf{i}+\mathbf{j}+\mathbf{k}$. **1**

These are the direction vectors of the two lines.

$(\mathbf{i}+3\mathbf{j}+4\mathbf{k}).(\mathbf{i}+\mathbf{j}+\mathbf{k}) = 1+3+4 = 8$ **1**

giving

$$\sqrt{1^2+3^2+4^2} \times \sqrt{1^2+1^2+1^2} \times \cos\theta = 8$$

$$\cos\theta = \frac{8}{\sqrt{26\times3}}$$

$$\theta = \cos^{-1}\left(\frac{8}{\sqrt{78}}\right) = 25.06..^\circ \quad \textbf{1}$$

$\therefore$ acute angle between lines = 25° **1**
to the nearest degree.

(b) At the points on l which are $5\sqrt{10}$ units from the origin we have $|\mathbf{r}| = 5\sqrt{10}$ **1**

giving $\sqrt{(s+2)^2+9s^2+16s^2} = 5\sqrt{10}$ **1**

Interpret the given condition as an equation to solve.

$s^2+4s+4+9s^2+16s^2 = 250$

$26s^2+4s-246 = 0$

$13s^2+2s-123 = 0$

$(13s+41)(s-3) = 0$

$s=3$ or $s=-\frac{41}{13}$ **1**

Hence, the required points have position vectors $\underline{2\mathbf{i}+3(\mathbf{i}+3\mathbf{j}+4\mathbf{k})}$ and

$\underline{2\mathbf{i}-\frac{41}{13}(\mathbf{i}+3\mathbf{j}+4\mathbf{k})}$. **2**

(c) At the closest point

$(2\mathbf{i}+s(\mathbf{i}+3\mathbf{j}+4\mathbf{k})-(6\mathbf{i}-\mathbf{j}+3\mathbf{k})).(\mathbf{i}+3\mathbf{j}+4\mathbf{k}) = 0$ **2**

The closest point has the property that its direction from the given point is perpendicular to the direction of the line.

$(\mathbf{i}(s-4)+\mathbf{j}(3s+1)+\mathbf{k}(4s-3)).(\mathbf{i}+3\mathbf{j}+4\mathbf{k}) = 0$ **1**

$s-4+3(3s+1)+4(4s-3) = 0$ **1**

$26s-13 = 0$ and so $s=0.5$ **1**

$\therefore$ The required position vector is

$\underline{2\mathbf{i}+0.5(\mathbf{i}+3\mathbf{j}+4\mathbf{k})}$ **1**

5 (a) (i) $\overrightarrow{OD} = \dfrac{\mathbf{b}+2\mathbf{c}}{3}$ $\qquad$ $\overrightarrow{OE} = \dfrac{3\mathbf{a}+\mathbf{c}}{4}$ **1**

These results are based on the formula for the position vector of a point dividing a line in a given ratio.

Answer	Mark	Examiner's tip

(ii) $\overrightarrow{AD} = \overrightarrow{OD} - \overrightarrow{OA} = \dfrac{\mathbf{b}+2\mathbf{c}}{3} - \mathbf{a}$

$= \dfrac{\mathbf{b}+2\mathbf{c}-3\mathbf{a}}{3}$ — 1

The position vector of any point on *AD* is given by $\mathbf{r} = \mathbf{a} + s(\mathbf{b}+2\mathbf{c}-3\mathbf{a})$ — 1

When $s = \tfrac{1}{9}$, $\mathbf{r} = \tfrac{2}{3}\mathbf{a} + \tfrac{1}{9}\mathbf{b} + \tfrac{2}{9}\mathbf{c}$ which — 1

therefore is the position vector of a point on *AD*.

Note that the direction vector has been taken as $\mathbf{b}+2\mathbf{c}-3\mathbf{a}$ rather than $\dfrac{\mathbf{b}+2\mathbf{c}-3\mathbf{a}}{3}$.

$\overrightarrow{BE} = \overrightarrow{OE} - \overrightarrow{OB} = \dfrac{3\mathbf{a}+\mathbf{c}}{4} - \mathbf{b}$

$= \dfrac{3\mathbf{a}-4\mathbf{b}+\mathbf{c}}{4}$

The value $s = \tfrac{1}{9}$ is found by inspection.

The position vector of any point on *BE* is given by $\mathbf{r} = \mathbf{b} + t(3\mathbf{a}-4\mathbf{b}+\mathbf{c})$ — 1

When $t = \tfrac{2}{9}$, $\mathbf{r} = \tfrac{2}{3}\mathbf{a} + \tfrac{1}{9}\mathbf{b} + \tfrac{2}{9}\mathbf{c}$ which

therefore is the position vector of a point on *BE*. — 1

Hence, the position vector of *G* is $\tfrac{2}{3}\mathbf{a} + \tfrac{1}{9}\mathbf{b} + \tfrac{2}{9}\mathbf{c}$. — 1

It has now been established that the given position vector lies on both lines and so represents the position of *G*.

(iii) $\overrightarrow{CG} = \tfrac{2}{3}\mathbf{a} + \tfrac{1}{9}\mathbf{b} + \tfrac{2}{9}\mathbf{c} - \mathbf{c} = \tfrac{2}{3}\mathbf{a} + \tfrac{1}{9}\mathbf{b} - \tfrac{7}{9}\mathbf{c}$

$\overrightarrow{OF} = \mathbf{c} + \mu(6\mathbf{a}+\mathbf{b}-7\mathbf{c})$ — 1

$= 6\mu\mathbf{a} + \mu\mathbf{b} + (1-7\mu)\mathbf{c}$

Direct comparison of the two results for $\overrightarrow{OF}$ is made easier by expressing both in the same form.

F also lies on *AB* so

$\overrightarrow{OF} = \mathbf{b} + \lambda(\mathbf{a}-\mathbf{b}) = \lambda\mathbf{a} + (1-\lambda)\mathbf{b}$ — 1

by inspection, $\mu = \tfrac{1}{7}$, $\lambda = \tfrac{6}{7}$.

Hence $\overrightarrow{OF} = \tfrac{6}{7}\mathbf{a} + \tfrac{1}{7}\mathbf{b}$ — 1

(b) (i)

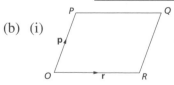

$\overrightarrow{OQ} = \mathbf{p} + \mathbf{r}$ $\overrightarrow{PR} = \mathbf{r} - \mathbf{p}$ — 2

The diagram helps to make the relationships clear.

(ii) $\overrightarrow{OQ} . \overrightarrow{PR} = (\mathbf{p}+\mathbf{r}).(\mathbf{r}-\mathbf{p})$ — 1

$= \mathbf{r}.\mathbf{r} - \mathbf{p}.\mathbf{p}$

$= OR^2 - OP^2$ — 1

$= 0$ (since $OR = OP$).

So *OQ* and *PR* are perpendicular. — 1